The Truffle Book

Gareth Renowden

LIMESTONE HILLS PUBLISHING

First published in 2005 by
Limestone Hills Publishing,
a division of Limestone Hills Ltd.
RD2 Amberley 8251
NEW ZEALAND
www.limestonehills.co.nz
info@limestonehills.co.nz

ISBN 0-473-10241-2 (softcover)
ISBN 0-473-10440-7 (hardback)

All photographs by the author unless otherwise credited.
Full photo credits on page 144. Author photo by Barry Flewellyn.
Front cover: truffle harvested at John & Iris Burn's truffière in Ashburton, New Zealand in July,
2005. It weighed 30 g and is shown at about twice actual size.
The quotation from Gustaf Sobin's *The Fly Truffler* on page 77
is used with the kind permission of Bloomsbury Publishing, London.
Editing and consultancy: Bradstock & Associates, Christchurch, New Zealand.
Design by Anthony Cohen (tony.cohen@moose.co.uk).
Layout and typesetting by Limestone Hills Publishing.
Printed in New Zealand by Spectrum Print, Christchurch.

CONTENTS

For Camille

FOREWORD

THANKS TO THE obsession of people like Gareth Renowden, the author of this book who I know personally and by name, I am glad to have "infected" others with the compulsive love of the fungi world and especially truffles. As a user of truffles for the last 50 years I can say that this is either an object of total love or in a minority of cases hate, but for certain there is no indifference about it.

Antonio Carluccio cooks porcini in the kitchen at Limestone Hills, May 2003

For someone to inject the spores of a variety of truffles in the roots of 200 trees is certainly the work of a fungi lover, because after having planted these trees there is still between 8 and 10 years of patient waiting time for nature to provide the rest.

In 50 years I must have dealt with about 1.5 tonnes of this tuber, which has delighted me, thousands of friends and customers of The Neal Street Restaurant in London.

I do hope that Gareth's project in New Zealand will be very successful and help spread the gospel in the Southern Hemisphere with the knowledge that should the fungus not find its popularity there, it can always be shipped to London!

Truffles are called black gold or diamonds and are the favourite food of gods, kings and pigs. Let's be piggish! Buona Fortuna.

Antonio Carluccio
Neal Street, London 2005

Introduction

I t's Camille's fault, this preoccupation of mine with truffles and mushrooms. If she'd been any sort of cook, then after our marriage I might not have become an untrained but enthusiastic chef, and I might not have slipped down the mossy bank of fungal obsession.

It's Antonio Carluccio's fault too. If the first recipe book Camille bought me after the wedding hadn't been his *Introduction To Italian Cooking*, larded with references to the joys of picking and eating wild mushrooms, then I might not have been tempted out into the woods of South West London in search of porcini and chanterelles. Without Antonio's glowing descriptions of their effects on food, I wouldn't have known about truffles.

It's also Mike Dash's fault, though he won't know it until he reads this introduction. If he hadn't taken his trying-too-hard-to-be-controversial trade paper columnist out to lunch in a Teddington restaurant that just happened to have a scribbled sign on the door that said "fresh truffles from Italy", then I wouldn't have ordered the risotto with truffle shavings on top, and I wouldn't have decided on the spot that this was one of the world's great tastes.

It's New Zealand's fault. The whole nation must bear its share of the blame. If Camille hadn't wanted to return to her birthplace, and I hadn't caved in so easily, then my transition from keen amateur mushroom hunter to hopeful professional truffle grower might never have happened. I wouldn't have stumbled on the property advertisement for a house with truffle plantation attached, and I wouldn't have phoned Camille to tell her that my whole life had been leading up to this.

And it's Ian Hall's fault, beyond any shadow of doubt. If I hadn't rung him up to ask for advice about truffle growing – Ian being the scientist who introduced truffles to New Zealand – then I wouldn't have driven out to Waipara to talk to a pioneering grower, and I wouldn't have stumbled on the old farmhouse with spectacular views and perfect soil where we have now put down roots, both literally and metaphorically. Ian hasn't exactly discouraged me in my obsession. Quite the opposite: he's encouraged me to add two more truffle species to my plantations, and a trial patch of pines infected with saffron milk cap mushrooms. He even brings people to see me and talk truffles.

Of course, blaming all these friends is the easy way out. I should really blame my genes. Those complicated twists of DNA hold the blueprint for the man I have become. Gifted from my parents come odd traits (like my father's ears) and strengths, and – if we are to believe current research – many of the characteristics of personality that make us who we are. I am obsessed with truffles because I am genetically predisposed to be obsessive. When humans lived in hunter-gatherer groups, there was probably some advantage in having old men around who knew a lot of obscure stuff, like which mushrooms were good to eat and which ones would kill you. These days that obsessiveness looks for an outlet wherever it can find one. Some men worship old cars; others collect Led Zeppelin concert bootlegs, neither of which would help much in the great outdoors. I grow ectomycorrhizal fungi. It's entirely natural, not at all eccentric, and has some survival value. More survival value than a Jimmy Page solo (unless you're Jimmy Page, of course).

On our back paddock, just beyond the young vineyard, we have a small truffière of a little over 200 trees, a mixture of oaks and hazels that have the Périgord black truffle, *Tuber melanosporum*, on their roots. They are in their eighth year, and should start producing truffles real soon now, as they say in America. Please bear in mind that this is not some capricious hobby. There is something that passes for commercial reasoning behind it all. Last season, black truffles were selling in New Zealand for as much as NZ$3,750 per kilogram (about US$2,400 or £1,400). We don't have to produce too many kilos before the income starts to look quite interesting. With the other New Zealand truffle growers, we hope to establish export markets, shipping our wonderfully aromatic produce to the world's finest restaurants during the northern hemisphere summer, when French, Spanish and Italian truffles are out of season.

On the front paddock, before you get to the olive grove, there are a couple of experimental truffle blocks. The smallest has oaks and hazels infected with the Burgundy truffle, *Tuber uncinatum*, and the bigger has oaks, hazels and a couple of pines inoculated with *Tuber borchii*, a white truffle known in Italy as the bianchetto. If we are lucky, and all our truffières bear fruit, then our truffle season will last six months, starting in autumn with the Burgundy truffle, progressing through winter with the Périgord black, and finishing in late winter with the bianchetto.

The celebration meal when we find our first truffle is already planned: truffled chicken (en demi deuil, perhaps), with a salad dressed by our own olive oil, accompanied by a glass of pinot noir from the vineyard. It's a long way from Teddington, but not as far as you may think.

CHAPTER ONE
The Truffle

I DREAD THE QUESTION "What's a truffle?", not because it's difficult to answer, but because when I start talking I know that some members of my family are going to begin rolling their eyes. They know the answer as well as I do, and will trot it out perfectly if given half a chance. But I'm not allowed to, unless I write a book about

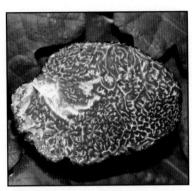

A ripe Périgord black truffle (Tuber melano-sporum) from Tasmania, cut in half. (Tim Terry)

it. Consider this book the answer you'd get if you bought me an extremely expensive truffle dinner (without children present) and then asked me to tell you everything I know about truffles. This chapter is the short answer — a glass of good wine's worth.

A truffle is a kind of fungus closely related to mushrooms, that grows under the ground. But instead of thrusting a typical mushroom cap up out of the ground to cast its spores to the wind, the truffle is a smelly bag of spores designed to be dug up and eaten by animals, which then scatter the spores around in their dung. The truffle smell that nature has designed to be so attractive to wild boar in the forests of Europe, is also very appealing to gourmets, and so these fungi have become revered in the cuisines of France and Italy.

Truffles appear in the soil around certain kinds of tree, because the fungus grows on and around the roots of those trees. The tree needs the fungus; the fungus needs the tree. Most kinds of truffle mature in autumn and winter. The summer truffle (obviously!) doesn't. Some truffles are black, some are white; some are nice to eat, others are unexciting or inedible.

The next most obvious question, usually accompanied by a knowing smile, is "Do you use a pig then?" The answer is no. Not even the French use pigs to find truffles very often any more, unless there's a TV crew in sight. Dogs are better. They are a wonderful example of biomechanical engineering, equipped with highly discriminatory sensors that make finding truffles rather simple (when they're co-operating), and they're happy with a piece of cheese or sausage or biscuit when they've done the job. A large sow prefers to eat the truffle, and won't fit in the back of a Deux Chevaux.

If your interest is already flagging, then at this point I might start to mention how pervasive the truffle scent can be. That will usually prompt the question "What do they smell like?", and elicit the answer "Old socks and sex." Go and find some unwashed socks – you'll need them for the next chapter. The problem with this explanation is that while I consider it fairly accurate, it isn't all that attractive an image. It doesn't do much to explain why truffles can fetch such high prices in the markets of the world. As an indication of just *how* high, in autumn 2004, a large Italian white truffle was bought by a London restaurant for £28,000/US$52,000 in a charity auction. Sadly, the customers who'd chipped in to the auction never got to taste it. The chef put it in a locked fridge and then went on holiday with the key. By the time he got back it had gone rotten. The regally-priced truffle was then flown back to Italy and given a royal burial, complete with pomp, ceremony and trumpets. The highest price ever achieved for New Zealand grown black truffles was equivalent to NZ$9,000/US$6,300 per kilogram, and we prefer to eat them before they go off.

To be fair, these prices are exceptional, but they do make people sit up and pay attention when I try to explain that truffle growing is a valid farming option in Europe, the USA, South America, Australia and New Zealand, and perhaps South Africa. In New Zealand there are more than 100 truffières, or truffle plantations, the oldest dating back to 1987. Seven of them have produced commercial quantities of truffle, and more are expected to begin production in the next few years. One of them will be mine, I hope. In recent years, new plantings of thousands of truffle-infected trees promise a future where New Zealand will export black truffle to the world. Australians, and Tasmanians in particular, hope to do the same — they have been planting large numbers of inoculated trees since the early 1990s — and there are schemes afoot to introduce truffle growing to South America and Southern Africa.

Why all this southern hemisphere interest? It's because our winter is the northern hemisphere summer. Our truffles are at their peak when the only truffle available to European, American and Asian chefs and gourmets is the preserved kind. Despite the prot-

Pigs are traditional truffle finders, as celebrated in this painted rock carving from the Musée de la Truffe in Sorges

estations of those who preserved them, truffles out of a can or jar are but a pale shadow of the fresh fungus. Use preserved truffles in a classic dish and you will wonder what all the fuss is about. And you will have paid through the nose for the privilege.

At this point, a warning for the consumer: look carefully at the label on the jar. Not only will the preserving process have reduced the essential "truffleness" but also, producers often use less aromatic truffles to begin with. Summer truffle (*Tuber aestivum*) is nice when fresh, but a lot more subtle than the Périgord black. The same is true of *Tuber indicum*, the Chinese truffle. And the classic white truffle of Italy, *Tuber magnatum*, is notoriously poor when preserved.

Southern hemisphere truffle growers hope that in the northern hemisphere offseason, their top-quality fresh truffle will find a ready market in top restaurants from Tokyo to L.A., New York to London, perhaps even Paris and Rome. We may even be able to sell them to French and Italian restaurants in the traditional

truffle homelands of Périgord, Provence, Piedmont and Bologna.
During the summer tourist boom, when people from all over the
world visit these delightful places, the availability of fresh truffle
could give the tourist the proper taste of the provincial cuisine, and
might even create extra demand for the French, Italian and Spanish
product.

In the world beyond Europe, truffles are seen as expensive delicacies. Buying fresh truffle at Fortnum & Mason in London or Dean
& DeLuca in New York is not for the faint of wallet, but the farmer
or truffle hunter who sold that same truffle in a French village
market will have received only a small fraction of the final price.
Inevitably, this means that truffle use is confined to restaurants
— and then only restaurants that can justify charging high prices.
When one of your ingredients is priced in dollars per gram, liberal
use is going to cost Conservative cash.

In France and Italy, where truffle hunting, growing and cooking
is an important part of regional culture, total truffle production
has been declining for years. At the peak of the truffle boom in
Périgord in the late nineteenth century, perhaps a thousand tonnes
of black truffle were been harvested in France. Today, despite the
planting of hundreds of thousands of truffle-infected trees, even in
a good season the harvest is likely to be less than a hundred tonnes.
That has to feed gourmets throughout the world, not just in Paris
and Provence, and so the pressure on prices is considerable.

Of course, if you happen to live in the Périgord, you will be able
to find truffles, or know someone who does. Even if you buy in the
market, you will not be paying layers of middlemen for the privilege
of getting your hands on the smelly fungus. Truffle can be a part
of your winter cuisine, one that's welcomed each year with church
services and blessings, street parties and fêtes. In countries where
the seasonality of fresh food is no longer defined by seasons but by
the fluctuations in the price, that may be hard to understand, but
truffles are a key part of regional life and self-image in many parts
of Europe. Even if the truffle market at Alba in Piedmont is full of
wealthy Germans who have driven across the Alps to try and lay
their hands on some *Tuber magnatum*, truffle still features on the
menu in local restaurants – and not just the ones that cater to tourists.

Down in the southern hemisphere, we have none of that truffle culture to guide us. With our largely Anglo-Saxon heritage, we
have a strong hereditary distrust of any kind of mushroom you
can't buy in a shop. We don't have the same long culinary traditions
that would enable us to get the most out of this scarce resource.

There are a few restaurants, hotels and upmarket lodges that buy everything we can produce, but the populace have yet to learn to welcome the truffle season in the same way that we look forward to the first oysters of the season or fresh asparagus in spring. Frenchmen can emote about the mystique and symbolism of the subterranean black diamond, wax lyrical about the impact of the aroma and the flavour, but in suburban New Zealand truffles are only an expensive mystery. It'll take a long time to change that, but in the meantime there's plenty of demand from overseas. At a time when New Zealand is lucky to produce 20 kg of Périgord black truffle in a season (June–September), one of the leading truffle growers regularly fends off people keen to buy 100 kg every week.

What is it about truffles that provokes all this devotion, that moves people to spend serious money on a taste and a smell? I shall attempt to find an answer in the next chapter...

CHAPTER TWO
The Empire of the Senses

IF YOU HAVE NEVER TASTED A TRUFFLE, this is going to be an ultimately unsatisfactory book. If I were writing about potatoes, most of my readers would know what one looks like. Many would know the names of a few varieties and the best way to cook them. But the fungal tuber is not something so well known. It is rated with caviar and vintage champagne as a gourmet ingredient, deeply expensive and rare, the realm of the fine restaurant and fickle chef. Not on the menu at McDonald's. Not obvious, like vanilla or aniseed. Subtle but powerful, ultimately unknowable – and almost unobtainable or unaffordable.

At some point, therefore, I have to explain what truffles taste like – the difference between black truffles and white truffles; why one is usually cooked and the other eaten raw (or barely warmed). I have to explain to you why they have such an elevated place in the pantheon of gourmet foods. You're going to have to try to imagine what I'm on about and recall things from your own experience that might offer some comparison. (I thought about providing a scratch'n'sniff cover, which might be a good idea for a bit of in-store promotion – instead of wheeling out the tired old author for a signing session, a few squirts of Truffarome could bring the crowds flocking... or perhaps not...)

Anyway, the stuff in the little scratch patch would be entirely artificial. Realistic, but nevertheless artificial. There are people who will tell you that if it smells like a truffle then it is the same as truffle, but I remain unconvinced. I have walked in the woods of Quercy, smelt the forest floor in Provence and Piedmont, dug my hands into the truffle soils of New Zealand, and the romantic in me knows that the these terroirs bring their own complement to the subtle mixtures that make up the taste and aroma of truffles. The scientist in me understands that evolution may have conspired to create a smell that attracts animals, and that once having discovered the secret of attraction, it would be very conservative. Any

In the famous white truffle market at Alba, assessing the aroma.

mutation that changed the magic formula would make it less likely that the fungus could successfully propagate itself. So the smell would stay pretty much the same. But what is to stop the fungus from responding to its environment — and its partner plant — by developing slightly different mixtures of complementary flavours and perfumes?

In the meantime, refresh your memory of the smell of unwashed socks — not a teenager's super-ripe school socks at the end of the week, but an adult's of a day or two's wear (wool and nylon mixture). Leave your armpits un-deodorised for a few hours on a warm day. Open the spice cupboard and take a deep sniff. Crush an unpeeled clove of garlic. Find some damp leaves and dig your fingers into the earth underneath (oak leaves are best). Then go for something floral — lilies for penetration, roses for sweetness. Store these smells away. We'll need them later.

It's hardly an original thought, but one has to wonder at the sanity of the people who first tried eating wild mushrooms. There are a few species that are very dangerous, a few that kill people every year when the uneducated or the foolhardy make mistakes. They are the reason that French chemists open on Sundays to check the baskets of mushrooms brought in by enthusiasts. Some mushrooms are deadly to man, but don't kill other animals. Truffles are more discreet, and stay hidden under the ground most of the time. When our ancestors were leaving Africa, encountering new environments as they expanded their range, they must have been expert at living off the land, hunting meat and gathering roots, nuts and berries. Without a written means of recording what they knew, there must have been a comprehensive oral tradition, with the knowledge to recognise good foods and the dangerous passed down from father to son, mother to daughter. As they expanded away from the savannahs and into deserts and woodlands and mountains and valleys, encountered deserts and snow, they must have been very quick to adapt to the riches around them. They probably used the same system taught on survival courses: try a little bit first, see if it makes you ill. If it doesn't, try some more. If it tastes good, you might speed up the process – or try feeding it to your dog. But someone must have been the first to try a truffle. What motivated him or her? Mere curiosity at these strange black things that attracted the wild pigs, or the strong smell? Did they eat them raw? It's difficult to imagine *Homo erectus* preparing tournedos Rossini.

As the last ice age retreated and forests began to reclaim western Europe, bands of human hunter-gatherers were spreading across the continent. They would have been just as smart as us, just as capable of spotting that wild pigs loved to eat things that grew under the ground around certain trees. Pigs are not exactly subtle when it comes to digging things up. They stick their snouts deep in the soil and plough forwards like hairy bulldozers, leaving behind a muddy mess. Perhaps a particularly observant Cro-Magnon person spotted a leftover truffle in all that mayhem, sniffed it, tasted it and enjoyed it enough to add it to the repertoire of stuff they hunted and gathered.

Thousands of years later, as civilisation was beginning to transform humanity and the world, the Greeks certainly knew their mushrooms and truffles. Theophrastus, a close friend of Aristotle's, and often called the father of botany, covers them briefly in his *History of Plants*. "This is also the mode of growth and the physical habit of these underground plants, such as the truffle, and the fungus which grows in Cyrene and is called misy." He doesn't mention much more, and his references to truffles "growing in sandy places" suggests that he may be describing desert truffles, not the black and white truffles of France and Italy. Much Greek wisdom was built on the knowledge assembled by the early civilisations that developed on the banks of the Tigris and Euphrates in modern Iraq, and in Egypt. Throughout the Middle East and North Africa, desert truffles are still highly prized.

The Romans were interested in truffles of all sorts. Desert truffles would have been most important: they can be found in Sicily, as well as around most of the Mediterranean, and their place in

Roman cuisine would have been inherited from the Egyptians. They used them as appetisers, and in salads dressed with herbs and *garum*, a salty fermented fish sauce. When Apicius wrote *The Art of Cooking* nearly 2,000 years ago, he provided several recipes for truffles, though his treatment of them seems extreme by modern standards, frequently involving boiling them before cooking them and serving them with sweet and salty sauces. Quite what this did for the delicate flavours of the fresh truffle is hard to imagine, but he was probably looking to beef up the flavour of the mild desert truffle.

The Romans were also great eaters of mushrooms, and certainly knew about the truffles of cooler climates. They used summer truffles and *bianchetto*, and probably also ate Italian whites and Périgord blacks, but we have little knowledge of how they cooked with them. Desert truffles carried all the prestige, so the domestic and regional truffles may have been seen as food for commoners, not nobles. That was certainly the case in the centuries after the collapse of the Roman empire.

The truffles we use today didn't begin their slow rise to the top of the food pile until the 14th century. They remained peasant food, grubbed up by the pigs as they foraged for acorns in the great forests of Europe. Things began to change in 1370, when the Duke of Berry, a French nobleman with an eye for the main chance, tried to impress Charles V with exotic new foods and tastes. He asked his wife, Jeanne d'Armagnac, to help out, and she provided truffles. They were white truffles – probably bianchetto or similar species, and "grey" truffles – probably summer or Burgundy truffles. They seem to have been a hit, for the Duke is known to have continued buying truffles for his banquets, but Périgord black truffles remained unappreciated by the great and the good.

French cuisine is supposed to have got a great boost when the Catherine de Medici, at the age of just 14, arrived from Florence in 1533 to marry the Duke of Orleans, the future Henry II. She brought with her paintings, crockery, solid gold cutlery, and cooks. Although Catherine was unpopular with the French people, her influence at the court on fashion and food was undeniable. Her sumptuous feasts were famous, and although she probably favoured Italian white truffles over the indigenous species, her refined cuisine had a lasting impact. When the first French cookbook, *Le Cuisinier François* was published in 1651, truffles were featured in more than 60 recipes. The author, La Varenne, famous chef to Louis XIV, did most to elevate black truffles, and particularly Périgord black truffles, to the culinary status they command today.

They also acquired a reputation as an aphrodisiac. In this, it was echoing the experience of many "new" foods. Tomatoes ("love apples") were touted as aphrodisiacs when they arrived in Europe from America, as were potatoes – although the latter was probably more of a marketing campaign to encourage their use.

When Jean Anthelme Brillat-Savarin was doing the research (a long life of eating) for his famous treatise *The Physiology Of Taste: Or, Meditations on Transcendental Gastronomy*, (published in 1825 shortly before his death, aged 70) he clearly devoted a lot of time to truffles. He addresses them in detail, and provides perhaps the best analysis of their supposed aphrodisiac properties. After recounting the tale of a woman who serves truffles in a fine dinner only to find that her male guest becomes distinctly frisky, and who is thereby convinced of the potential for these fungi to excite the amatory faculties, he convenes a committee of experts: "I consulted men in whom professionally great confidence is placed; they formed with me a committee, a tribunal, a senate, a sanhedrin, an areopagus, and we gave the following decision to be commented on by the literary men of the twenty-fifth century:- 'The truffle is not a positive aphrodisiac, but it may under certain circumstances render women more affectionate, and men more amiable.'" We've got some way to go before we get to the 25th century, but when we do, Brillat-Savarin will still be absolutely correct.

He was ahead of his time, too, in noting that truffles were most popular with certain classes of professional person: "the doctors of the law, who, *caeteris paribus*, consume more truffles than any other class of citizens." Lawyers have always, it seems, had a lot to answer for. Medical men don't escape either: "Doctor Malonet used to eat enough to give an elephant indigestion. He however lived to be eighty-six."

The end of the 19th century was the golden age of the black truffle in France. Production was at its peak, and although still a luxury, it was not so expensive that the rich couldn't use them in profusion. Prince Curnonsky, the great gourmand, when asked by a hostess how he liked his truffles, replied, "In great quantity, Madam; in great quantity." In Britain, Mrs Beeton's first cookbook, published in 1861 and aimed squarely at the new Victorian middle class, could countenance a dish of truffles in champagne, requiring only a "dozen fine black truffles". Unlike many of her other recipes, however, she provides no estimate of the cost, noting only that truffles "are not often bought in this country". Not a dish served very often today, either. A moment with a calculator and current market prices suggests that the ingredients alone would cost hundreds, if not thousands, of pounds, ecus, or dollars. A billionaire's feast, these days, rather than a special-occasion dish for the middle class.

Since that heyday, black truffle production has declined markedly. Prices have risen steeply, reinforcing their position as an expensive gourmet treat. France was probably harvesting around a thousand tonnes of black truffle a year at the end of the 19th century, but can only manage a few tens of tonnes in a good year today.

So what is it that gives truffles their prestige? Is it simply a matter of scarcity and price? Or is it what they do to food? You can find people who don't like truffles, just as you can find some who don't like caviar. One French researcher suggests that as many as 50 percent of people don't find the smell or taste of truffles to be particularly attractive. I'm married to one of them, which is a bit of a pity for both of us. I suspect that estimate is a bit high, not least because many hopeful eaters will not have experienced the full majesty of the truffle's effect on food. My wife, for example, may have been put off by a particularly foul truffle sorbet she once tried. You don't find many recipes for truffle sorbet, and there's a good reason for that.

To really experience truffle, whether the glories of *Tuber magnatum*, the Italian white, or the grandeur of *Tuber melanosporum*, the Périgord black, you have to have good fresh ripe truffle. This is not a trivial point, not even in the heart of truffle lands like France and Italy. Many things can go wrong between dog and table: the truffle may not be properly ripe – or worse, it may not be the right truffle. Chinese truffles look a lot like Périgord truffles but have only a slight scent and flavour, but they are available at a fraction of the price. The temptation to pass them off as the real thing is huge, especially with the aid of a few drops of truffle oil. And there are other, lesser species which can find their way into the unwary buyer's basket.

The other really important factor is the restaurant, and of course, the chef. If the restaurant is good, and the chef knows what he's doing, you'll get a good truffle meal. This is probably easier on mainland Europe than elsewhere in the world – especially in the truffle producing regions – because there's a good pool of knowledgeable customers who will not put up with second best. I cannot imagine the chef at the *Auberge de la Truffe* in Sorges daring to use anything but the best. The same is true at the most famous restaurants, whether drawing on French or Italian inspiration, in the world's major cities. Marco-Pierre White, the hugely successful British chef, buys as much as 100kg of black truffle per *week* during the season. His supplier will not want to let him down.

The problem lies with chefs who think they know what they're doing, but don't. Even if they manage to get their hands on good truffle, a moment's inattention in the kitchen can see all the precious aroma disappearing up the enormous stainless-steel extractor fans. Or they may believe that any truffle is a good truffle, and expect a summer truffle to be as good as a Périgord black, or the Chinese truffle to be an acceptable stand-in. Both have their place in dishes, but not as the soloist in a symphony of flavours. This sort of chef exists all round the world, and is a real peril. One expensive but unimpressive dish, and a wary diner may write truffles off as a costly waste of time.

The increasing use of truffle oil, memorably described by Anthony Bourdin as "the tomato ketchup of the middle classes", also plays a rôle. Truffle-flavoured oil does smell and taste a lot like the real thing, and is available all year round. Why worry about the fickle fungus, confined to its season and available only at great expense, when a few drops of oil can give a dish some of that truffle cachet? It's a reliable way of giving customers an idea of what all the fuss is about. There is a risk, though, that by having the truffle experience in a bottle, to be drizzled over any dish, it becomes just another flavour to be played with; another element in some fusion cuisine fiction. I have seen, in a restaurant that should (and does) know better, the travesty of offering a summer truffle dish with truffle oil added to boost the flavour. Why bother with the fresh truffle at all?

Do I use oil? Yes, to train my dog. Will I eat dishes with truffle oil in them? Yes, provided the oil is not being used to replace real truffles, and is used sensitively.

Something of the same issue surrounds the use of preserved truffles. These have been on the market for over a hundred years, and for a long time were the only way that anyone could taste truffles out of season, or a long way from the producing areas. But the preserving process reduces the flavour, so their impact in a dish is much less than a fresh truffle. Preserved black truffles are better than preserved white truffles, but both are expensive. They can give you an idea of what truffles are like, but not the full picture.

Truffle oil and the many truffle-flavoured products that have come on to the market in the last few years are not necessarily bad, but they can lead to unrealistic expectations when you encounter the real thing. They offer a consistent experience, one you can guarantee to taste in the dish, but they are almost all entirely artificial and have seldom been anywhere near a real truffle. They offer a simplified picture, a sort of cartoon version – bright and colour-

ful but ultimately false. Their flavour profile is determined by food
chemists, not the delicate interplay of fungus, soil, tree and climate.
The truffle aroma and flavour is that of an average truffle, some
sort of idealised *magnatum* or *melanosporum*. Out in the real world,
truffles vary in flavour, not just by species and by ripeness, but by
the place they're grown.

This is a controversial subject, however. There are those in the
business who will insist that all Périgord black truffles taste the
same. On one level, this is true — they will all have the same family of flavours, just as all Rhône wines made with the syrah grape
will taste like Rhône syrah. But the wines will taste of lots of other
things as well, reflecting what the French call the local *terroir*: that
combination of soil, climate, site and culture that is unique to each
vineyard. European black truffles that are shipped around the
world are not designated by region. They will come from all over
France, Spain and Italy. The box that arrives in New York could
contain truffles from four countries, and they won't have little
labels telling you which is which. Their aromas will have tended to
blur into each other during the trip. The buyer has little chance of
picking up what might be quite minor nuances.

There have been some experiments conducted in France, but
they have produced mixed results. One has shown that experienced tasters can detect qualitative differences in taste and aroma
between truffles grown in the Tricastin region of southern France,
and those sourced from Spain and Italy. On the other hand,
another trial couldn't find much difference between French truffles grown on different soils. Some growers will tell you that their
truffles often have varying aromas; others dismiss the idea. There is
some (rather enjoyable) research to be done, and I look forward to
the day when the truffles of North Canterbury will be recognised
as the tastiest in New Zealand.

So what do *real* truffles smell and taste like? What do they do to
food to make them worth their considerable cost? There is a huge
difference between a Périgord black truffle and the Italian white
truffle, but they have one thing in common. When ripe, their smell
is strong. Leave a ripe truffle in the fridge overnight, and if you
haven't taken the precaution of sealing it in something completely
airtight, everything else in the fridge will smell of truffles. Every
time you open the fridge door, the kitchen will smell of truffles. If
you have a lot of truffles, you need a second fridge. The smell can
be overpowering, a sledgehammer on the nostrils. In high doses, it
isn't subtle.

The Italian white truffle has a very penetrating and powerful,

The Italian white truffle, **Tuber magna tum**, *on offer at Alba The big one in the middle was broken while digging it out o the ground, and has been put back togeth- er with rubber bands It's more valuable that way.*

earthy, garlicky aroma. It is not usually cooked, but shaved on to relatively bland dishes such as a *risotto Milanese*, simple *tagliatelle* or fried eggs. You might stir some slices into an omelette as it is cook- ing, but you wouldn't cook the truffle: all the aroma and flavour would be driven off. Restaurants will make a fuss about shaving the truffle on to your dish at the table, but the cost of the things means that you will not get very many slices. Luckily, a little goes a long with *Tuber magnatum*. Appreciate the aroma, the perfume, first, and then stir your slices into the rice or pasta. As you eat, you will find the aroma translates into a sort of intense mushroomy, earthy taste, and that taste will intensify as the meal progresses. What's more, you will be reminded of the taste and smell by what Oregon truffle scientist Charles Lefevre calls "the famous truffle burps". When I had my first *magnatum* experience at a lunch fifteen years ago in London, I continued tasting truffle for most of the evening. And during my research tour of Italy, after a week of enjoying truffles at every opportunity, I could have sworn that the aroma was oozing from all my pores.

The Périgord black truffle can be handled in the same way as *magnatum*, served sliced raw over simple dishes, but it can stand the rigours of cooking much more than its Italian cousin. The aroma of *melanosporum* is less garlicky, more musty and sweet, a very intense mushroom smell overlaid with other notes, especially what wine tasters call "forest floor". Its effect on food isn't as dominating as the Italian white. It co-operates with the flavours in the food, enhancing and intensifying them. A steak with truffle sauce becomes more meaty, eggs are transformed into a gourmet item, and every aspect of the meal becomes more satisfying. If that sounds over the top I apologise, but it is precisely because truffles can do this that they are worth paying large sums of money for. And because a little goes a long way, a talented chef can give his guests an experience worth any small premium he may charge.

Other black and white truffles suffer in comparison with the two fungal stars, but they can be worthwhile in their own right. The summer and Burgundy truffles are cousins to *melanosporum*, with similar but less strong flavours. Good ripe examples are very worthwhile, and because they are much cheaper, can (and should) be used in greater quantity. Mrs Beeton's truffles in champagne might be feasible with *aestivum* or *uncinatum*. The only white truffle that gets anywhere near *magnatum* is *Tuber borchii*, the *bianchetto*. When properly ripe, it is often passed off as *magnatum*, and when preserved it retains much more of its flavour. But it is not yet traded widely beyond Italy. Our New Zealand experiments with this species are going to be fascinating, and even if we can only produce truffles that give half of the true *magnatum* experience, I for one will be very pleased.

CHAPTER THREE

The Realm of the Roots

THERE'S AN AWFUL LOT OF FUNGUS in the world. It's been estimated that the total biomass of fungi is around twice that of all animals. The world's largest living thing is a honey fungus called *Armillaria ostoyae*, growing in the Malheur National Forest of eastern Oregon in the USA. It lives in the forest floor, covers an area of 890 hectares, and has been slowly killing trees for more than two thousand years. If it weren't for fungi, we wouldn't have yeasts to make bread or beer, or the moulds that give blue cheese its piquancy. There are at least 1.5 million species of fungi, and they can be found in the oceans, fresh water, and soil. Their spores can circle the planet on the wind. They've been around for a billion years. They cause athlete's foot. They're not plants and they're not animals, and they're incredibly important to life on earth.

Fungi can't make their own food. They have to absorb their nourishment from living or dead organic matter, sometimes by co-operating with plants, or by breaking down the decaying bodies of microbes, animals and plants. Organisms like fungi which recycle the nutriment in dead matter are said to be saprobic, and help ensure that the earth's ecosystems function as they should.

The relationships between fungi and plants are just as important. Nine out ten plant species have to grow in association with a fungus if they are to thrive. Cabbages, nettles and fast-growing annual weeds are among the few that manage without. What we think of as plant roots are usually in fact a complex mixture of fungus and plant: a mycorrhiza — a "fungus root" in Latin. The plant needs the fungus, and the fungus needs the plant. The fungus helps the plant to get nutrients from the soil, and in return gets carbohydrates from the plant. It's an example of symbiosis, and it's not new. There's fossil evidence of mycorrhizae from as far back as 460 million years ago.

The body of a fungus consists of very thin strands called hyphae.

These grow into the roots of the plant and out into the soil, greatly increasing the surface area of the root system. There are two main kinds of mycorrhizae. Vesicular-arbuscular mycorrhizae are formed by most of the plants used in agriculture. The fungus grows inside the roots of the host plant, and pushes hyphae out into the soil. These fungi don't form mushrooms. Truffle species are ectomycorrhizal: the fungus coats the outside of the plant rootlets like a glove, and then grows into the cells of the root tip, forming a skeleton of cells called a Hartig net. The effect on the root system is dramatic. In young pine seedlings, 80 percent of the surface area of the root system is provided by fungal hyphae, even though they only amount to 20 percent of the mass. Hyphae are much thinner than root hairs, and are able to grow out into the tiniest pores in the soil. To give you some idea of the difference this makes, one gram of soil can contain anything up to 20 metres of hyphae. As a result, the efficiency of the plant's nutrient uptake is increased enormously. Mycorrhizae are particularly important in mobilising phosphorus for the host plant, and can also help with nitrogen. In exchange, the fungus gets carbohydrates from the plant – sugars produced by the solar-powered factories we call leaves. As much as 20 percent of a plant's production of carbohydrates can be transferred down into the mycorrhizae, giving the fungus the energy it needs to do its job — and to propagate.

The relationship between plant, fungus and soil is very complex. In order to extract nutrients for the host plant, many ectomycorrhizal fungi produce chemicals and enzymes which modify the soil structure and chemistry. Populations of 'helper' bacteria live in association with the mycorrhizae, benefiting from the fungal activity, and also helping it along. Most of the energy for all this activity comes from the plant via the carbohydrates pumped down into the mycorrhizae. In fact, this energy and carbon flow is essential in creating and maintaining a healthy soil structure.

Mycorrhizae also help the plant in other ways. They help protect the roots from pathogens such as *Fusarium*. Chemical warfare down in the soil has led fungi to evolve antibiotics such as penicillin, which have transformed medicine over the last century. *Tuber melanosporum*, the Périgord black truffle, has a habit of killing or stunting any plants that try to grow in its mycorrhizal zone, producing the characteristic brulée, or "burnt" zone round the host tree. There is some evidence that the fungus may be feeding on these plants, but at the very least it's helping to keep competition for nutrient resources down.

The benefits to the plant can be enormous. This was convincingly

demonstrated in Puerto Rico in the 1950s. Attempts to establish pine plantations on the island had been made since the beginning of the century, but all failed. Pine seedlings would establish well at first, and grow up to 10 cm high, but would then die. The island lacked any of the symbiotic fungi the pines needed to establish mycorrhizae. In 1955, soil from pine stands in South Carolina was brought over and was worked into the soil round 32 unhealthy-looking one-year-old seedlings. Another 32 were left untreated. A year later, the treated trees were 1.5 metres tall and had active myc-orrhizae, while most of the others had died.

More than 4,000 species of fungi form ectomycorrhizal relation-ships, mainly with woody plants. Trees such as oaks, beeches, birch-es, eucalypts, poplars and willows, and shrubs such as rock roses act as hosts. Fungi in this group produce some of the most popular mushrooms of traditional and haute cuisines, including *Boletus edu-lis*, better known as porcini in Italy or cèpe in France, *Cantharellus cibarius*, the chanterelle, and of course truffles. Some species of fungi have a narrow range of hosts; others can grow with many. *Pisolithus tinctorius*, the dye-maker's puffball, is known to form ecto-mycorrhizae with 46 species of tree belonging to eight different genera. It is particularly good at helping its host to survive in low soil moisture conditions – as is the Périgord black truffle.

Soil conditions also determine which fungi are present. Some prefer acid soils, others alkaline soils. Wet soil suits some fungi and not others. A single tree can have dozens of different fungi forming mycorrhizae with it, and a single fungus might form mycorrhizae with several trees, effectively linking them together under the ground. In one experiment, a Canadian researcher proved that fungi could actively move material from tree to tree. Carbon absorbed by one tree could end up in a neighbouring tree — even in a different species of tree. As much as six percent of the carbon fixed by one tree could be moved to a neighbour. That's enough to make the difference between a tree producing seeds or not. In effect, the fungus seemed to be "managing" the trees it was growing with.

The ultra-fine hyphae that make up the fungal body are often invisible to the naked eye, but they can merge to produce various kinds of structures. The honey fungus (*Armillaria spp*) is a killer of trees and an enemy of many gardeners and foresters. It's also known as the bootlace fungus, because it produces black stringy structures called rhizomorphs as it spreads through the ground around the plants it's attacking. Sex, however, spurs some fungi on to greater things: mushrooms, truffles, puffballs and other kinds of fruiting bodies, all designed to propagate the species. All fungi reproduce by spores, tiny single-celled "seeds" that germinate to produce a new individual. Mushrooms and truffles are a means of getting those spores scattered away from the parent individual to where they may find the right conditions to infect a new host.

The familiar mushroom, a stalk with a cap on top and gills underneath, is an umbrella sheltering a spore factory. You can demonstrate this quite simply. Pick a mushroom (a shop bought mushroom will do fine, provided the cap has opened), and place it gill-side-down on a piece of paper. Cover it with a glass or bowl to keep draughts out, then leave it overnight. In the morning the spores falling out of the cap will be visible as very fine dust forming a pattern on the paper.

A typical mushroom shape: cap with spore-producing gills underneath, propped up on a stalk. This is the first saffron milk cap (Lactarius deliciosus) grown at Limestone Hills in 2005.

Not all mushrooms have gills, however. Boletes, such as porcini, have a sort of sponge underneath the cap, made up of thousands of fine tubes that shed spores. *Hydnum repandum*, called pied de mouton (sheep's foot) by the French and hedgehog mushroom by the British, has fine white spikes under its cap. All of these structures shed spores into the air. The dispersion technique used by puffballs is pretty obvious from the name. They're basically bags of spores

that mature and dry out, eventually splitting and puffing their
spores out onto the wind. Try kicking a mature puffball, and you'll
be amazed at the amount of spores that come out — especially if
it's a giant puffball (*Calvatia gigantea*).

Truffles are a lot more subtle. Their spore-spreading technique
relies on getting the co-operation of animals, and it's the persua-
sive means they use to attract the attention of burrowing or forag-
ing animals that makes them interesting to gourmets. In technical
terms, animals are vectors for the dispersal of the spores — an
important part of the cycle that links plant, fungus and animal.
Like puffballs, truffles are basically bags of spores. As they mature
underground, they begin to develop their characteristic aroma.
When ripe, they can be sniffed through several feet of soil by crea-
tures with good noses. The animal then burrows down, eats the
truffle, and later spreads the spores around the forest floor in its
droppings.

This reproductive strategy seems to be highly successful and
rather common. There are hundreds of species of truffles, or
truffle-type fungi, found all over the world. In the USA, squirrels,
rodents and deer all dig for truffles, and researchers have estimated
that as many as 60 different species may be eating them. For some
animals they may be a seasonally important staple. In Australia, 80
to 90 percent of the diet of the rare long-footed potoroo consists
of truffle-like fungi, and the Tasmanian bettong eats as many as 49
different species of truffles. In some cases passage through animal's gut, followed by a spell in the rich surroundings of its faeces,

Partially-excavate
truffle, close to a
hazel root. The soil
all around this frui
body smelled very
strongly of truffle.
Some of the small
hazel rootlets at the
top of the truffle sh
signs of being myco
rhized with truffle
fungus.

may be required to persuade the truffle spores to germinate.

If getting animals to eat you is your reproductive strategy, then you have to find a way of attracting their attention. The Périgord black truffle, *Tuber melanosporum*, uses a combination of at least 50 different chemicals to create an aroma that is both powerful and penetrative. These include dimethyl sulfide, acetaldehyde, 2-methyl-1-propanal, 2-methyl-1-butanal, ethanol, 2-methyl-1-propanol, 2-methyl-1-butanol, and acetone, but there are also many more complex molecules in the mix.

As a truffle ripens, the ground around it becomes saturated with smelly chemicals, until it reaches the air and spreads on the wind. At the sorts of concentrations that animals can detect, most humans don't notice a thing, but if you stick your nose into the hole left when you've just dug up a truffle the smell can be overpowering. All truffles have a sort of family smell: they use much the same arsenal of chemicals in different mixtures. The most important of these is dimethyl sulfide (DMS), a fairly simple molecule which consists of two methyl (CH_3) groups linked together by a sulfur atom. This is a very smelly substance — a strong odorant is the technical term — which has a sharp, green-cabbage-like smell at high concentrations. It's the same chemical which gives cooked cabbage its distinctive smell. Despite this unpromising description, it is widely used as a perfume base. There are several isomers of DMS and one, called DMS-d6, has a less cabbagey and more truffle-like smell than the basic molecule. French research has shown that the smell of DMS is the main means by which mammals scent truffles, while truffle flies and other insects track them down by smelling other organic sulfides that are present.

In the early 1980s, a group of German researchers discovered a steroid compound called androstenol in black truffles. Androstenol is a sex hormone found in male pig saliva, and also in the underarm odours produced by human males. Wild sows, they reasoned, might be sexually attracted to the smell of ripe truffles. If this was true, then this might explain the truffle's reputation as an aphrodisiac in humans. A nice story, and speculation quickly became received wisdom. Sadly, the truth is more prosaic. Women seldom admit to being turned on by unwashed armpits, and research by Thierry Talou, the leading expert on truffle aroma, showed the theory to be false. He synthesised an artificial truffle aroma cocktail, leaving out the androstenol, and showed that pigs were just as motivated to dig for that smell as they were for fresh, ripe, expensive truffle. That cocktail of chemicals, entirely artificial, is now widely used to create so-called truffle oil or "truffle-infused" oil. Fresh truffle is a very expensive raw material, and oil naturally infused with truffle aroma is less impressive – because the aroma is less strong – than oil that's been dosed with a synthetic mixture. The next time you see truffle oil on a menu, bear in mind that it will almost certainly never have been anywhere near the real thing.

Fruiting time varies between species. The Périgord black truffle, *Tuber melanosporum*, ripens in mid-winter; the Italian white, *Tuber magnatum*, in late autumn and early winter. *Tuber aestivum*, the summer truffle, can be found from early summer until autumn, while its close relative, *Tuber uncinatum*, is an autumn truffle. Some truffles grow quickly to full size, and ripen more or less straight away. Others, like *melanosporum*, take a while to grow to full size and then months to ripen. Each species occupies its own ecological niche, preferring different host plants, with varying soil conditions and climatic requirements. Some are found deep in forests; others on the edge.

Like most fungi, they need some combination of warmth, moisture and light to get fruiting under way. The host tree also has something to do with it, because it supplies a lot of the energy underpinning the process. How these factors interact in different truffle species is not understood in any great detail. When research identifies the precise formula for triggering *melanosporum* production, I for one will be a happy trufficulteur. Moisture has an obvious role to play. When France has a dry summer, black truffle production in the following winter is poor. Wetter or average summers give better crops – one reason why French truffle growers have been keen to install irrigation in their truffieres. But *melanosporum* also requires heat and sunlight (or the heat provided by sunlight), whereas *magnatum* likes moist, shady stream-sides or valley bottoms.

The truffle year begins in spring. Weeks before the host plants show signs of new leaves, their roots will have begun growing, and the fungal mycelium will have increased its activity. As the new leaves begin to turn sunlight into sugars, and the plant resumes its growth, the mycelium begins to benefit from this influx of energy. The Périgord black truffle will begin to do its host the favour of suppressing weed growth in the rooting zone, producing the characteristic ring or patch of stunted plants or bare soil. This is called the brulée, or 'burnt ground', and becomes clearer as summer progresses.

Most truffles, in common with most ectomycorrhizal mushrooms, begin the fruiting process in late summer to autumn, after rain. By this time the host plant has plentiful reserves of carbo-

Typical truffle soil in the Périgord: a thin layer – 10-20 cm – of darker soil on top of fractured limestone.

hydrate for the fungus to use. In autumn, before the leaves fall, trees pump a lot of this carbohydrate and nutrients into storage in the root system, dramatically increasing the food supply available to the fungus. That's why a damp autumn often brings out huge swathes of mushrooms in woodlands.

Once the truffles are ripe, they sit in the ground ready to be eaten. If they are, then the spores are dispersed by their animal vectors. Any uneaten truffles simply rot in the ground, but this may not be a total waste. It means that spores are readily available to grow a new mycelium the following spring, when the host plant sends new roots out. The truffle spores may help to re-infect the host and give the truffle fungus a competitive advantage over other fungi whose spores are also present. Some European truffle growers even leave or bury damaged or rotting truffles in the ground for this purpose, calling it "seeding". After fruiting, the fungus takes a winter break, surviving in and around the dormant root system.

The spores that have been distributed in animal dung may end up near a suitable host plant – either a young seedling tree or a bit of the rooting zone of an older plant – so that they can re-establish the symbiotic growth of the mycelium.

All the major groups of ectomycorrhizal fungi include some truffle-like or hypogeous (beneath the earth) species. This suggests that the truffle "lifestyle" must convey some significant advantages, in certain conditions, over the more normal method of casting spores to the wind. The process by which truffles evolved is only speculative, but we can have a fairly good guess at what must have happened. All mushrooms start life as little lumps in the mycelium. As they enlarge, they push up through the soil until they emerge from the surface. At this stage, they are often roughly egg-shaped, at least when viewed from the top. They then expand and differentiate into different zones: stalk, cap and, underneath the cap, a zone where the spores are formed.

One major drawback of this process is that the fungus has to put a lot of effort into building a large and complex spore distribution structure, requiring lots of energy. It's also vulnerable to its environment, drying out in hot sun or wind, being eaten by insects or larger animals (including humans), even kicked over by wanton passers-by. Truffles, on the other hand, are just bags of spores that have to synthesise some smelly stuff to attract the animals. A fungus that by some chance mutation had its development stunted, might have had a competitive edge over others that carried on growing big mushrooms. And if they happened to attract animals by being tasty and smelly, then so much the better. Over millions of years, you might end up with the truffle and truffle-like species we see (or dig up) today. Fossil evidence suggests that fungi were adopting the hypogeal lifestyle over 400 million years ago.

CHAPTER FOUR

The World of Truffles: France

TRUFFLES OF ONE KIND OR ANOTHER can be found on every continent, except Antarctica (not noted for its forests), but the heart of the truffle business is in Europe. France and Italy dominate truffle cuisine, and together with Spain produce most of the truffles eaten round the world. Attempts to grow the main European truffle species are being made in Britain, the USA, Australia and New Zealand, with Chile, Argentina and perhaps South Africa likely to follow. China's production of cheap *melanosporum*-look-alike truffles has had a major impact on the world market in the last decade, but that hasn't been without its problems. The world of truffles is a big and complex place, full of wonderful stories. We start with France...

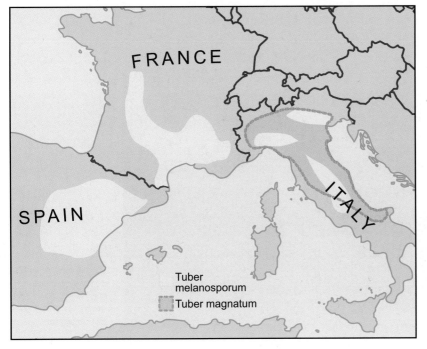

FRANCE

ITALY

SPAIN

Tuber melanosporum
Tuber magnatum

The main truffle regions of Europe stretch from Spain through France and down through Italy. Périgord black truffles can be found in all three countries, but the Italian white is much more choosy about where it grows.

For the French, the king of the truffle world is *Tuber melanosporum*, the Périgord black truffle. It's found throughout south-west and south-east France, wherever there are oaks, limestone soils and sufficient heat. A broad swathe of the western Massif Central, from Limoges towards Toulouse through the Dordogne, Lot and Tarn is prime truffle country. Many of the small villages have truffle markets, of which Lalbenque's (near Cahors) is probably the most famous, but you can visit St Alvère's on the internet.

In the south-east, the Tricastin region around Oranges and towards Mont Ventoux, and the hills and valleys of the Luberon – that part of the south of France made famous by British writer Peter Mayle – are where the truffle business is most concentrated. The markets at Carpentras and Richerenches are the best known, and the village of St Saturnin les Apt is well worth a visit, as we shall see.

The association of the Périgord name and black truffle is something of an historical accident, or perhaps an early example of clever marketing. Today, most of France's black truffle is produced in the south-east, but at the end of the 19th century Périgord had the market sewn up.

Truffles were well established in the cuisine of the French aristocracy by the 18th century, but there had been no systematic attempt to cultivate them. Scientists of the time couldn't agree whether they were simply a kind of vegetable or something that grew on the roots of the trees. One even believed they were swellings on tree roots caused by fly bites. Down in the woods, however, astute peasants had a better idea of what was going on. In 1811, Joseph Talon,

Périgord truffle country: oak trees in a neatly maintained truffière outside Lalbenque.

from the hamlet of Croagne, close to the village of St Saturnin les Apt in the Luberon planted some acorns on a stony patch of hillside. The trees were for firewood – or so he claimed. Oaks take a long time to grow, so he was obviously prepared to be patient, or trying to mislead his neighbours. He may have heard of the experiment in the middle of the previous century, when Monsieur de Montclar, a local nobleman, collected acorns from Malta and planted them on land he owned around St Saturnin. Some years later, those oaks produced truffles, but the French revolution intervened, and the trial was all but forgotten.

Talon harvested his first truffles after six or seven years, and then set about buying up more poor, stony patches of land and planting them with acorns. He kept his technique a secret for a while, but as the baskets of truffles he took to the market in Apt grew bigger, so his neighbours got more interested. It is said that his cousin, also called Joseph Talon, was the spy who finally cracked his secret, and before long truffle plantations were being established in many parts of the south-east.

Talon's technique worked because he was planting his acorns in places where truffles occurred naturally. As the seedlings germinated and put their young roots down into the soil, they became associated with the fungi already growing there, or with spores that were waiting for a suitable host to come along. If there was black truffle around, they became infected with that, but there were plenty of other fungi around to interfere. Talon made the best of his hit-and-miss method not by picking acorns from producing trees, but by planting in places well suited to black truffle. A refinement of his technique is to germinate the acorns in the brulées around productive trees, and then transplant the seedling, hoping that the truffle fungus will come with it. Even so, not all his trees produced truffles. Yields may not have been large by the standards of today's truffieres, but Talon was producing truffles from plantations, and an industry was born.

News of Talon's technique spread around France. By the 1840s, experiments in truffle growing had already started in the Périgord, but it took an agricultural disaster to get things really

Joseph Talon commemorated in stone in his home village of St Saturnin les Apt. "Lou rabassiè" is Provençal dialect for truffle hunter.

moving. In 1868 phylloxera began its devastation of France's vine-yards. Peasants who had been growing grapes could no longer rely on this steady source of income, and were forced to look around for alternatives. In the Périgord, where the vineyards were hacked out of the oak forests, vines were ripped out and oaks either re-planted or allowed to re-colonise the land. In 1876, the Conseil Général of the Dordogne was offering the equivalent of a subsidy to people who planted truffieres, and within 15 years truffle pro-duction began to increase dramatically.

Other factors fed the truffle boom. A process for bottling or canning truffles without boiling off all their taste and perfume was developed by Nicolas Appert at the end of the 18th century. Preserved truffles could then be shipped round the world. The spread of railways had a dramatic impact on the availability of agri-cultural produce, and fresh truffles could find a national and inter-national market. With a shelf-life of a week or a little more, a ripe Périgord truffle could easily be sent to Paris, London or Berlin.

By the end of the century, France was producing somewhere between one and two thousand tonnes of truffle every year. A wave of wealth spread through the Périgord, and you can still see the large houses built with truffle money in the little villages around Cahors. Some them are reputed to have been built with the pro-ceeds from a single year's harvest. Stories are told of growers hav-ing so much truffle to carry to market that they had to use donkey carts. Today a small bag or wicker basket is usually more than big enough. Truffle wholesalers, bottlers and canners prospered, and large factories were established to handle the avalanche of black gold. The words Périgord and truffle became inextricably linked, and remain so to this day.

Then things began to go wrong. Until the First World War, pro-duction remained substantial, averaging over 600 tonnes per year. In the 1920s and 30s, production plummeted to 250–350 tonnes per year, and by the 1960s had dropped to 80 tonnes per year. Today, production rarely exceeds 30 tonnes. What had been an affordable luxury product became increasingly expensive.

Several factors played a part in this decline. Although the truf-fle entrepreneurs who planted trees in the boom years of the 19th century knew that truffle would usually follow tree, they had only rudimentary ideas about how to manage production once it had started. Little oaks became big oaks, shading the ground in the truffieres, perhaps changing the environment to the benefit of other fungi. Some have suggested that the natural lifespan of truf-fle production in an oak truffière is about 35 years; others suggest

*Hugues Martin,
St Alvère truffle
grower, emerges
from his carefully
restored shepherd's
hut, called a
gariotte. He uses
it as a nighttime
"hide" when he's
trying to deter
poachers.*

that after that amount of time, tree and fungus have depleted the
soil of some key nutrient and so production declines. Whatever the
real reason, that length of time seems to fit the facts, and would
explain why the decline started in the early years of the 20th
century.

The First World War brought another problem. More than 1.3
million French people died in that war, and a further 4.2 million
were wounded. Rural France was badly hit. Women whose men had
gone to war couldn't manage all the truffieres, and so production
declined steeply as pruning and soil work ceased. After the war,
production improved, but never recovered to pre-war levels.

France, like all industrialising countries, also experienced the shift of rural populations to the cities. Traditional rural life changed, and this had a marked effect on the forests of France. What we think of as wild forests were actually intensively managed resources. Firewood was cut, trees coppiced to produce crops of poles and sticks for fences, paths were cleared, pigs, sheep and goats grazed. As the people left the countryside, the old ways were gradually lost, the forests became choked with undergrowth, and conditions that favoured the truffle were gradually lost. As the older generations died off, they took valuable knowledge with them.

The Second World War had much the same effect as the first. Production declined further, and never recovered. In the 1950s and 60s, the process of urbanisation and the movement of rural people into the towns accelerated. There was, however, a growing awareness of what was being lost. By the 1970s, preserving rural traditions, and especially regional foods, had become trendy. It started becoming fashionable to move back on to the land, either with an overtly green, self-sufficiency agenda, or as a romantic return to rural roots.

Scientific advances in the 1970s led to the production of trees artificially infected with *Tuber melanosporum*. They were heavily promoted and widely planted, and continue to be used to this day. However, despite hundreds of thousands of truffle trees being planted, there has been little if any increase in truffle production. This doesn't mean that planting infected trees doesn't work. There are plenty of productive truffières that have been planted in the last 30 years. It simply means that if that effort hadn't been made, French production today might be virtually nil.

France without black truffles is impossible to imagine, and the French will never let it happen. The black truffle is embedded deep in the national cuisine and in the regional cultures of Provence, Périgord, Burgundy and beyond. Every year, the start of the harvest is a cause for celebration. Villages have fêtes, churches hold masses, and truffle grower societies hold solemn marches and investitures. Restaurants add truffles to their menus, and the winter truffle markets begin. Poachers haunt the truffieres and country roads, while trufficulteurs and police stand watch with guns, flares and night-vision goggles. The rivalry can become so fierce that truffle dogs are stolen or poisoned. Intrigue meets culinary passion, and justice sometimes suffers. I've been told that several notorious Périgord poachers routinely escape unpunished because they are brothers of a local magistrate. One grower fires parachute flares when he suspects poachers are around, hoping to catch them in the act.

As prices rise and supply drops, the crooks become bolder. In recent seasons, shipments of truffles have been hijacked at gun-point. Night vision goggles have been adopted by poachers and by the police trying to catch them. The French truffle growers' association has seriously considered using GPS tracking systems to allow them to track stolen truffles. The cost is prohibitive at the moment but it won't be long before some combination of GPS and perhaps RFID (little chips that act like a radio barcode) will be used to identify and track shipments. I prefer the low-tech system proposed by Provençal truffle grower Jean-Marie Rocchia. He plans to drill little holes in his truffles and insert a note that says, "This truffle was stolen. Please report the person you bought it from to the police." Over the 2004/5 winter season, raids on truffières and dog stealing have become a virtual epidemic. Rocchia reckons that as the natural truffières of the French countryside have gone into terminal decline, and the value of truffles has gone up, the less scrupulous truffle people have turned to crime. In one incident reported by *The Independent* a poacher was shot in the buttocks by an angry, shotgun-wielding trufficulteur:

The poacher claimed that he was just strolling through the plan-tation, Rocchia says.

"If so, why was he doing so at night? And why was he kneeling with his head to the ground and his bottom in the air when he was shot? Do you know who he turned out to be? The president of the truffle association of a neighbouring département."

The two men – aggrieved truffle-grower and wounded truffle-rustler – screamed at each other publicly at the next truffle market. No further action was taken by either of them.

The "mélano" is not the only truffle produced in France, but it is the one that grabs all the headlines. *Tuber aestivum*, the summer truffle, and *Tuber uncinatum*, the Burgundy truffle, are both exten-sively harvested and traded. *Aestivum* has a black skin, but pale white flesh, and is a very close cousin to *uncinatum*. It can be found, when conditions are right, from spring to autumn, and often over-laps with the Périgord black season. It has less aroma and flavour than the Périgord black, but is still a good truffle to eat. It occurs throughout Europe, and is harvested in large quantities, so the price is not as exorbitant. *Uncinatum*, on the other hand, is found around Burgundy, and is an autumn truffle. It looks very similar to *aestivum*, but when ripe its flesh is brown, and the aroma and taste are stronger. Over the last few years, there has been a considerable growth of interest in this truffle, led by French scientist Gerard Chevalier. Infected trees are available, and truffières are being planted in France, Sweden and New Zealand.

Tuber brumale, also called the truffe musquée, looks a lot like *melanosporum* but is a lesser truffle with a slightly musky, bituminous scent and an earthy flavour. It grows in the same sort of conditions as *melanosporum* but has a wider climatic tolerance (it has been found in Britain), and will out-compete the black truffle if conditions are right. It ripens at the same time as the Périgord black and is harvested alongside it, but commands a much lower price. An unwary buyer might not notice the difference until too late, but regulations at all the major truffle markets are supposed to ensure that brumale is not passed off as mélano. True connoisseurs of truffles will tell you that a stray brumale will ruin the taste of any proper truffle dish, but brumales are still traded, and even imported into France for use in charcuterie and conserves.

If brumale presents the less scrupulous truffle salesman with a temptation, the Chinese truffle, *Tuber indicum*, is irresistible. This truffle (which I cover in a later chapter – see p. 70), is cheap and available in large quantities during the winter truffle season. It looks and smells very like *melanosporum*, but lacks the power and finesse of the real thing. It first appeared in French markets in the early '90s, but in the 1994-95 winter season it has been estimated that total imports to France were double the local production. Very little was sold as Chinese truffle. It was being bought in China for FF150 per kilo, shipped to France for about FF350 per kilo, and then sold into the trade - particularly restaurants - for up to FF1,500. This was a lot cheaper than real *melanosporum*, which was selling at the time for about FF2,500, but enough to give the seller a mammoth profit. Not surprisingly, trufficulteurs were enraged.

Chinese truffles: available by the sackful at bargain basement prices in markets in the Yunnan province of China.
(Yu Fuqiang)

Since those dark days, the Chinese truffle has been tamed somewhat. There is still a risk that black-market truffles might not be what you expect, but there are other, more significant risks to the French truffle business. What if a truffle-tree nursery, by accident or by penny-pinching design, used a Chinese truffle to infect its seedling trees? The Chinese truffle could find its way into French truffières and start displacing the real thing. French scientists have recently developed a DNA technique for testing truffle trees and distinguishing between Chinese truffle, truffe musquée and the real black truffle, but this may have come too late. There have been reports that Chinese truffles have now been found in French truffières, and there are indications that the species is highly competitive, able to displace the much more valuable *melanosporum*. It's too early to say how serious this problem might be, but the French business certainly faces challenging times.

CHAPTER FIVE
Italy

IF FRANCE IS THE LAND OF THE BLACK TRUFFLE, then Italy is the kingdom of the white. The Italian or Piedmont white truffle, *Tuber magnatum*, is the truffle that attracts most of the attention and commands the highest price of any truffle in the world. It's associated with the Piedmont region of northwest Italy, and in particular with the market town of Alba, but just as Provence produces most of France's Périgord blacks, so other regions of Italy produce more *magnatum* than the Piedmont.

Tuber magnatum is found in the wild from Piedmont, along the southern slopes of the Po valley as far south as the Adriatic coast and the Marche, in parts of Tuscany and Umbria, and further south in the Abruzzo and Molise. It also grows in the Istria peninsula of Croatia and some other parts of Slovenia and Serbia, the southern part of the Ticino canton of Switzerland, and possibly in a few small pockets of France close to the Italian border. Despite intensive efforts over recent years, it has never been successfully cultivated, so the truffle business is built on a vast network of tartufaio (truffle hunters), who comb the best spots from October until the end of December. The Périgord black truffle, known in Italy as the tartufo nero pregiato (valuable black truffle), likes oaks, heat and limestone. *Magnatum* prefers moisture, deep soils and valley bottoms. It creates no pianello (brulée), and so the hunter relies on a dog (or pig) to lead them to the truffle. It prefers different host trees, especially poplars, willows and the European lime.

Tuber magnatum has featured in Italian cooking since at least the Middle Ages. Pope Gregory IV, who headed the Catholic church in the 9th century, requested a meal of truffles to strengthen him in his battles against the Saracens, who took possession of Sicily during his reign, and seemed interested in the rest of Italy. The Dukes of Savoy, who ruled over the Piedmont, certainly thought highly of *magnatum* in the 14th century, and Catherine de Medici is thought to have brought a love of Italian white truffles to France

Tuber magnatum, the Italian white truffle, offered for sale in the traditional way in the truffle market in Alba, Piedmont. Truffles are often individually priced and displayed on white tickets.

with her when she married the future Henry II in 1533. That didn't have much impact on the French, however, and they stuck to their black truffles.

This preference has never changed. Those who believe that French cuisine is the finest expression of the culinary arts hold that the Périgord black truffle is the best truffle. Italian food lovers maintain that *magnatum* is simply without peer. French cognoscenti will grudgingly concede that the Italian white truffle commands the highest prices, but are snooty about its aroma and flavour. The *Larousse Gastronomique* isn't exactly full of praise: "The white truffle of Piedmont has a slight flavour of garlic which goes well with some dishes." Italians will admit that the black truffle is good, but are sure that the white truffle is better. Only one Frenchman, to my knowledge, has publicly admitted the superiority of *Tuber magnatum*, and that's Provençal trufficulteur Jean-Marie Rocchia in his book *Des Truffes en général & de la Rabasse en particulier*. I have no idea whether he can still hold his head up in public.

Perhaps it has something to do with the nature of the two cuisines. French cooking, in the tradition of La Varenne and Escoffier, loves complex and refined sauces. Périgord black truffles work well in that sort of situation, reinforcing flavours and standing up to the heat of the kitchen. Italian cuisine is not built around highly refined and formal food. It is less overtly complex, more focused on the quality of ingredients and the power of individual flavours. *Magnatum* doesn't respond well to cooking, and its powerful aroma and flavour are used as the focus of a dish, complemented by milder things like pasta, rice and eggs.

Other factors have helped to cement *Tuber magnatum's* place as the most expensive truffle. It is only harvested from the wild, and then only in parts of Italy and the former Yugoslavia, so the supply is very limited. In a good year, production might reach 50 tonnes, but markedly less if there's been a drought. Prices regularly exceed US$2,000 per kilo. There is also considerable demand from overseas, from the Italian diaspora. There are probably as many people of Italian descent living overseas as there are in Italy. Between 1870 and 1970, 27 million Italians emigrated to the USA, Australia, Argentina and many other countries. They took their regional cooking with them, and Italian restaurants were often the focus of these expatriate communities. The love of the white truffle was exported, and became an important part of the cuisine of the Italian diaspora.

Clever marketing played an important part in putting the white truffle on its pedestal – and also established Alba's place at the centre of the business. In the 1930s, Giacomo Morra, the owner of the Savoy Hotel in Alba, began calling *magnatum* the "white truffle of Alba", and the name stuck. Morra's master stroke, however, was to give big truffles away to important people. If conditions are perfect, *magnatum* can sometimes produce huge fruiting bodies. In 1949, Morra sent a particularly fine example to Hollywood star Rita Hayworth as a present, gaining considerable publicity in Italy and the USA. He capped that in 1951 by sending a huge truffle weighing 2.52kg to President Harry Truman. It remains the largest truffle ever found. Morra neglected to mention the fact that it had been found near San Miniato, in Tuscany.

Morra's marketing campaign continued for years. Marilyn Monroe got her truffle in 1954, and in 1961 Morra rather cheekily sent one to General de Gaulle. Astronauts have received them, as well as plenty of Italian TV and film stars, and at least one pope. Alba became as firmly linked with white truffle as Périgord was with *melanosporum*.

Large white truffles are now often sold off in charity auctions, fetching huge prices and, perhaps not coincidentally, generating lots of press coverage. In 2004, an 850g white truffle, also found near San Miniato, was auctioned off for £28,000 to the London

Clever marketing by Giacomo Morra built Alba's reputation as Italy's truffle capital. On the banner he's described as "king of truffles" and pictured with one of the giant truffles that he sent round the world. Note the large street sign in three languages pointing to the market.

restaurant Zafferano. Unfortunately, the chef locked the truffle in the fridge before going off for a week's holiday. When he got back, it was inedible. He buried it in his garden, but when the good burgers of San Miniato heard of the truffle's fate, they demanded it be returned to Italy and buried with due honours. So it was exhumed, flown to Italy, and buried with considerable pomp and ceremony and a fanfare of trumpets. Rather embarrassing for the restaurant, but marvellous marketing for *magnatum*.

Alba is a small medieval town surrounded by hills. If it weren't for truffles, it would be best known for the wine made in the little towns and villages scattered on the hills around it. Barolo, regarded as one of Italy's finest red wines, is made nearby. In clear autumn weather, the view from the Piedmontese hills to the snow-capped alps to the north-west is stunning. So is the smell in the truffle market.

When I toured Italy in autumn 2000, the market was being held in a large tent in a piazza surrounded by a maze of small streets. The place was packed with tourists and locals out for their Saturday morning shopping. I could have found the market by nose alone: truffle was in the air, like some finger beckoning me on. Inside the tent, the smell was overpowering. I spent half an hour in there, sniffing, fondling, and photographing, but I needed to get a breath of fresh air every ten minutes. It wasn't subtle, that smell. Nor were the prices. White truffle was selling for about US$2,000/£1,400 per kilo. It seemed that most of the people in the market spoke German. They'd driven over the Alps for a truffle weekend. Nice, if you can afford it.

The Alba truffle salesmen would undoubtedly like you to believe that all their wares are locally sourced, but this is far from the truth. *Magnatum* from all over Italy is sold there, because Alba has established itself as the premier marketplace. The other major market is Acqualagna, but like France, there are many smaller markets in truffle-producing areas.

Although collecting and eating *magnatum* has been a feature of North Italian life for hundreds, if not thousands of years, it is only in the last few decades that truffles from further down the spine of Italy, especially in the Molise region, have been commercially exploited. One tartufaio from the north apparently stumbled on the fact that large quantities of excellent *magnatum* could be harvested in the area, and over the next few years, he and a few select friends made several small fortunes. Their clear run to riches came to end when one of the team let a little too much slip after a heavy night in a bar. There is still a possibility that *magnatum* may be growing in other parts of Italy or its immediate neighbours. If you have no truffle-hunting tradition, or if you ignore white truffles, as the French do, then you may never know about the treasure under your feet.

Alba may be world famous, but Acqualagna, close to the old town of Urbino in the Marche, has its own claim to fame. Locals maintain that apart from producing more white truffle than the Piedmont, they can also serve truffle all year round. On the hills around the town, it's possible to look down into valleys where *magnatum* is found on the valley floor and in shadier wooded parts, while *melanosporum* is found on the sunnier limestone slopes facing

Italy's top truffle scientist Alessandra Zambonelli (and Tuberina) in typical white truffle country. Dense shady damp woodland in the hills and valleys to the west and south of Bologna.

south. When the *magnatum* season ends at the end of December, they are already serving the first of the tartufo nero. When that season ends in March, they have good supplies of the bianchetto, *Tuber borchii*, a white truffle that may not be quite as good as *magnatum*, but is sometimes good enough to pass off as the real thing by the unscrupulous. From May to November, they also have supplies of scorzone, the summer truffle, *Tuber aestivum*. The tourism promoters may be stretching things a little with respect to late spring and early summer, but it's a nice claim to be able to make.

Numerous attempts have been made in the last 20 years to find a way of producing *Tuber magnatum* in plantations, but all have failed. There are occasional reports that an experimental plantation has produced some, but nothing definite ever percolates through the scientific community. Part of the problem is that *magnatum* is a slippery customer as truffles go. When *Tuber melanosporum* infects the roots of its host plant, it's relatively easy to see what's going on. I can dig up a rootlet and see the little black "sausages" of mycorrhiza on the root tips. *Magnatum*, on the other hand, looks like a lot of other white truffle infections, and has proved very reluctant to infect seedling trees when nurseries use the methods that work for *melanosporum* or bianchetto. Many of the experimental *magnatum* plantations may have been infected with bianchetto by mistake, or the truffle may require ecological conditions that are very hard to replicate in a plantation. Whatever the problem, it's proving a tough nut to crack.

Tuber melanosporum truffieres are being planted in many regions of Italy, and while their produce isn't as prestigious on the local market, there are plenty of buyers in France who will pay good prices, as well as several local canners and bottlers. The black truffle is most strongly associated with Norcia, a small town in Umbria, and has a significant place in the regional cuisine.

Beyond the "big two" truffles, there are others that are harvested and eaten, though some are really only local delicacies. The bianchetto or marzuolo truffle, *Tuber borchii*, is readily available and is now being grown in truffieres. *Tuber brumale*, known as tartufo invernale, is harvested but doesn't command a premium price; and the same is true for its close cousin, the tartufo moscato, *Tuber brumale* var. *moschatum*, also known as the musky truffle. The summer truffle, *Tuber aestivum* (tartufo estivo or scorzone) is common throughout Italy and widely traded, whereas *Tuber macrosporum*, the smooth black truffle (tartufo nero liscio) is not much valued. *Tuber mesentericum*, the tartufo di Bagnoli, is similar to the summer truffle, but has a rather intense bitumen or phenolic smell and is really only enjoyed around Bagnoli Irpino, a little town in the province of Avellino Campania, inland from Naples.

CHAPTER SIX
Spain

PÉRIGORD BLACK TRUFFLES can be found in the oak forests that cover a large part of central and north-east
Spain, especially in the triangle formed by Valencia,
Madrid and Barcelona. Over the last 50 years, the country has become one of the world's most important producers of
Tuber melanosporum. An average year sees around 15-20 tonnes pass
through the markets – roughly the same as France, and perhaps
double the Italian production.

In stark contrast to France and Italy, whose cultures have been
steeped in truffles for thousands of years, Spain has no history of
truffle appreciation. The Moors, who ruled Spain in the Middle
Ages may have appreciated the desert truffles that grow in the
south, but the rest of the population never seems to have bothered
with either kind. That changed in the 1950s. With French production declining sharply, and road and rail links opening up the
Spanish countryside, enterprising French truffle businessmen were
soon wondering why there shouldn't be truffles in the limestone
plateaux of Catalonia and Aragon. As soon as they started looking,
they found them.

The natural forest of the region, called Monte Bajo in Spanish, is
an open scrubby mixture of black pines, juniper and evergreen oaks
(specifically *Quercus ilex* ssp. *ballota* - the holm oak). The limestone
plateaux average about 1,000m above sea level, and the altitude
compensates for the extra heat that comes from being closer to the
equator than the truffle regions of France and Italy. *Tuber brumale*
and *Tuber aestivum* also occur naturally. The natural truffières of
Spain represent the stronghold where *Tuber melanosporum* survived
during the last ice age. As the ice retreated and the forests expanded again, the fungus spread north into France with its host trees.

The Spanish truffle trade grew rapidly in the 1950s. Locals soon
learnt the art of finding truffles, markets sprang up, and trade
with France boomed. Likely-looking areas were explored to see if

the valuable fungi were present, and experimental truffières were planted. In some areas, local government has taken an interest, encouraging truffière planting by subsidising the cost of infected trees. But the largest experiment was the brainchild of Salvador Arotzarena, a businessman who'd made money in food processing and who had a lifelong interest in mushrooms and truffles. In the late 1970s he started planting an enormous truffière at Navaleno, near Soria (about 200km north of Madrid). It now covers 600 hectares (1,550 acres), and is planted with more than 400,000 evergreen oaks. It has a large nursery for producing infected trees, a team of 20 truffle dogs, and is said to produce around 3 tonnes of truffle a year – a sizeable chunk of the world's total production. Arotzarena died in 1996, but his truffière continues to expand.

Few others have had Arotzarena's confidence (or money) and typical truffières are much smaller: a few hectares at most. But there has been a significant expansion of truffière planting in the last decade, particularly towards the southern end of the truffle's range in Valencia. A case in point is the little town of Sarrión, south of one of the major truffle markets at Teruel (inland from the city of Valencia). The local growers' association, founded in 1997, has grown from 12 to 148 members, and the local business supports seven truffle-tree nurseries, with two more in Teruel. The local council has estimated that as much as 10 percent of the productive land is now devoted to truffle production – almost 1,400 hectares. Most of the truffières are still young, but as they come in to production, Spanish exports will get a healthy boost.

Teruel hosts one of Spain's biggest truffle markets. Unlike the French and Italian markets, which are held in daytime and in public places, Spanish truffle-trading is done late at night, in bars and cafés. Saturday night is Teruel's night and it has been estimated that as much as half of Spain's output may pass through it – a tonne or more every week. The market at nearby Morella is held on Friday nights, and handles half the volume of its neighbour. In Catalonia, the old town of Vic hosts an active market, as does Molina de Aragón in Castilla la Mancha.

CHAPTER SEVEN
Britain

THE BRITISH ARE NOT NOTED as a nation of fungi lovers. Generally they assume that any mushroom is poisonous unless it looks like a field mushroom or comes from a supermarket. When I began hunting wild mushrooms and serving them for dinner, my wife was convinced that either we were all going to die or that I was plotting to get rid of her. I succeeded at neither. It may therefore come as something of a surprise to British readers to learn that from the 18th to the early 20th century there was a moderately thriving truffle business based on the summer truffle, *Tuber aestivum*.

The beech woodlands on the chalk downs of Kent, Surrey and Hampshire were the prime focus for the business, but *aestivum* occurs naturally in most parts of the UK, certainly as far north as Lothian in Scotland. It is the commonest edible truffle, but not the only one. *Tuber brumale* has been collected in southern England, and *Tuber borchii*, the bianchetto of Italy, occurs over much the same area. Today, very few Britons have the skills required to find truffles, and wild boar are not exactly plentiful, so any truffles that aren't eaten by other animals must rot in the ground. Someone with a properly trained dog and the persistence to rediscover the prime locations might be able to create a good little business.

British truffles can, when conditions are perfect, occur in profusion. In September 2004 a farming family in Little Bedwyn, a village on the Wiltshire/Berkshire border, dug up 10kg of summer truffles, and found it easy to sell them to local restaurants. One sign that there's something interesting underground is that squirrels will scrape away at the earth to get at them. They'll also leave little scraps of truffle around for the alert hunter to spot.

But the easiest way to find them is to have them growing in your garden. A family in Minchinhampton in Gloucestershire saw squirrels scraping at their lawn, dug up what they were after and found a summer truffle. Antonio Carluccio reports in his book *A Passion*

For Mushrooms that a lady in Kent harvests truffles every year around an oak in her back garden. I'd like a garden like that.

In the early 18th century, Professor Bradley, the head of the botany department at Cambridge University was much taken with truffles: "They are very plenty in our Woods in England, as I understand by several who have found them this Summer by my Directions, and I believe will be much more so, since several curious Gentlemen have followed my Advice in propagating them."

In Victorian England, truffle harvesting was carried out more systematically. Dogs and pigs were used, and truffles were widely available. Mrs Beaton, however, wasn't terribly impressed in the first edition of her great cookbook:

Britain's first Périgord black truffle trees were planted by Nigel Hadden-Paton in 1999 at his estate in Hertfordshire.

"In this country, the common truffle is found on the downs of Hampshire, Wiltshire, and Kent; and they abound in dry light soils, and more especially in oak and chestnut forests. In France they are plentiful, and many are imported from the south of that country and Italy, where they are much larger and in greater perfection: they lose, however, much of their flavour by drying. Truffles have in England been tried to be propagated artificially, but without success."

Professor Bradley's directions were obviously unhelpful.

Shortly after the First World War, a farmer called Arthur Savory published one of the classic descriptions of English village life. In his account of the village of Aldington, near Evesham in Worcestershire, he recorded one of the last accounts of an English truffle hunter in action:

"In some counties, but not so far as I am aware in Worcestershire, one of the harmless snappers-up of unconsidered trifles is the truffle-hunter. At Alton, in Hampshire, one of these men appeared in summer; he carried an implement like a short-handled thistle spud, but with a much longer blade, similar to that of a small spade but narrower; he was accompanied by a frisky little Frenchified dog, unlike any dog one commonly sees, and very alert. The hunting ground was beneath the overhanging branches of beech-trees, growing on a chalky soil; the man encouraged the dog by voice to hunt the surface of the land regularly over; when the dog scented the truffles underneath, he began to scratch, whereupon the implement came into use, and they were soon secured. I have since been sorry that I did not interview this truffle-hunter as to his methods and as to his dog, for I believe he is no longer to be seen in his old haunts. But I did get a pound or two to try, and was disappointed by the absence of flavour. I have since read that the English truffle is considered very inferior to the French."

Savory may well have been describing Britain's last truffle hunter, Alfred Collins, who worked around the Winterslow area of Wiltshire, and might well have strayed over the border into Hampshire. Collins was aided by two Spanish poodles that he used to carry around with him in two hand-crafted leather baskets attached to his bike. These he trained by rubbing their noses with truffle, and then tying them to an older dog that knew what it was doing. They could, apparently, sniff truffles up to 20 metres away, but Collins could also trace truffles by the clouds of small flies they attracted, and sometimes even by feeling them under the surface of the soil with his feet. In the early 1920s truffles sold for 2/6d (12.5p) per pound, which might not sound like much today, but was a lot at that time, especially if you consider that on a good day, he could collect 25lbs (11kg) of them. By the time Collins retired in 1930, the price had risen to 5/6d (27.5p) per pound, but that obviously wasn't enough to keep him in business. So died a family business, one that merited a Royal warrant. His father had once found a truffle that weighed 2lbs, and in a piece of marketing genius that foreshadowed Morra in Alba (see p.44), he sent it to Queen Victoria. History does not record if she was amused.

Alfred Collins carried his poodles around in twin panniers on his bike.
(Craig McNeill)

Truffles were principally foreign exotica for the next 50 years, something expensive found on French and Italian menus, supplied from overseas and affordable only by the wealthy. But there was a huge change in British eating habits over that same period. From the rationing of the immediate post-war years (which ended just as I was born), to the "food as fashion" boom of the 1980s and 90s, British cuisine moved from being the laughing stock of Europe to setting world standards. In 2005, influential US food magazine *Gourmet* declared London to be the best place to eat in the world. And the truffle hunters may be about to make a return.

Nigel Hadden-Paton is keen to encourage the revival of the British truffle business.

In the late 90s, ex-Army major Nigel Hadden-Paton and chartered surveyor Adrian Cole, both lovers of eating truffles, decided that there was a business opportunity in encouraging British farmers to plant truffières. They obtained a license to use tree-infection technology developed in New Zealand, and set about producing trees infected with both Périgord black truffle and Burgundy truffle. Burgundy truffles, *Tuber uncinatum*, are genetically identical to the summer truffle, so there is no reason why truffières shouldn't succeed over a large part of the UK. Returns, even given the relatively modest prices summer truffles fetch, should be very attractive, especially at a time when farming is under all sorts of pressures. The Périgord black, however, is a more speculative venture. It grows in parts of France that are significantly warmer than any part of England, but Hadden-Paton believes that if sites are chosen carefully, the Périgord black could fruit successfully. Carefully chosen, sheltered locations on south-facing slopes could have enough heat – and global warming should help things along too. He put his own money on the line, and planted his own truffière in an old walled garden on his Hertfordshire farm. And when he sold that farm and moved to the west country, he had the trees dug up and shipped to a new site.

Hadden-Paton and Cole's company, Truffle UK Ltd, has generated a lot of interest from farmers and press over the last five years, and considerable numbers of infected trees, mainly hazels infected with *Tuber uncinatum*, have been planted. There are now truffières near Salisbury, Wiltshire and in the heart of the Cotswolds, near Moreton-In-Marsh. More are planned for Somerset, Kent and Norfolk. There are even rumours of Royal interest, and truffles may soon be popping up at one or two famous estates. In a real coals-to-Newcastle situation, Truffle UK has bought land in prime French truffle country and planted it with trees from Britain.

They may not have things all to themselves for long. A keen young scientist called Paul Thomas has been attempting to enter

A young Burgundy truffle truffière near Tring in Hertfordshire, planted with trees supplied by Truffle UK. (Adrian Cole)

the truffle-tree nursery business. His scheme to produce trees infected with *melanosporum* and plant them in France was featured on the BBC's venture capital TV programme *Dragon's Den*, and though it looked as though he might have found backing, the deal fell through. He hasn't given up though, and hopes to have trees available in the next few years.

CHAPTER EIGHT

North America

THE GREAT TRUFFLES OF EUROPEAN TRADITION don't turn up in the wilds of North America. Efforts to cultivate them are under way and have been reasonably successful, but the continent also has its own, very intriguing contingent of edible truffles, both white and black. The heart of North America's truffle world is Oregon, in the Pacific Northwest. There, in the great Douglas fir forests of the coastal mountain ranges that stretch from northern California to British Columbia, you can find the Oregon white truffle and the Oregon black truffle. There are two main kinds of Oregon white truffle; *Tuber oregonense*, the Oregon winter white truffle (which used to be called *Tuber gibbosum* var. *autumnale*), and *Tuber gibbosum* itself (sometimes called the Oregon grey or Oregon spring white truffle). *Oregonense* is an autumn and winter truffle. Fruit bodies can be found from October through to February, but only become fully ripe in December, while *gibbosum* ripens from February until early summer.

Oregon winter truffles on sale in a local market. Finding good ripe examples can require a lot of sniffing. (Charles Lefevre)

Tuber oregonense is a relatively small truffle, with a brownish interior and orangey-brown skin when fully mature. It can be prolific, and there is a thriving trade serving mainly local restaurants and markets. At their best, Oregon whites stand comparison with the Italian white truffle, having a complex, powerful aroma and plenty of flavour. Local truffle expert Dan Wheeler describes them as having "aromas of butter, fresh-roasted hazelnuts or filberts, dried morels and sometimes garlic". In a recent comparison, another local expert, Charles Lefevre, tested perfect Oregon whites against some *Tuber magnatum*, and the Oregon truffles won hands-down (although he admits the former may have been past its best). When you take into account that he paid $100 a pound for the Oregon truffles and $1,800 a pound for the Italian, the contest seems distinctly unfair. He insists however, that you should never buy *oregonense* before December, or you risk disappointment. Despite that, Oregon white truffles have a reputation with some people as being rather weak and not very worthwhile.

A young Douglas fir platation –prime hunting ground for all the Oregon truffles. (Charles Lefevre)

Commercial harvesting is done by raking through the soil in likely-looking spots (often marked by tell-tale squirrel, deer, or small mammal scrapes). This is an effective technique from the collector's point of view: a bit of hard work can yield lots of truffles that can sell for $200 or more per kilo. In the mid-90s it was estimated that over 6 tonnes a year were being collected in this way. Unfortunately, raking means that unripe truffles are just as likely to be collected as ripe ones, and an unripe truffle is a disappointment. This has led some chefs and consumers to write off the Oregon white truffle as lacking in aroma or flavour, but if they've never tasted a ripe one, they haven't had the proper experience. It's also fair to say that this truffle needs careful handling: once fully ripe it doesn't have a long shelf life, and unless stored carefully it can develop a strong and unpleasant chemical flavour.

The spring version, *Tuber gibbosum*, is similar from a culinary point of view, and often grows larger than *oregonense*, but is seldom collected commercially. There is obviously considerable potential to use it to extend the truffle season, leaving only high summer without a supply of fresh local truffle.

The Oregon black truffle is a completely different beast. It doesn't belong to the *Tuber* genus that contains the other important culinary truffles. Sometimes called the Chartreuse truffle, it has the Latin name *Leucangium carthusiana*, and grows in the same Douglas fir forests as its two white compatriots. It is normally larger than the white truffle, ranging from walnut- to baseball-sized, and has a very dark skin and flesh. The aroma, according to the North American Truffling Society, is "a strange mix of pineapple, port, mushrooms, rich soil, and chocolate". Several local experts rate it as the best of the Oregon truffles, and at least the equal of the French black. It isn't as well known as the white, however, because it hasn't been extensively harvested. It prefers slightly different soil conditions, so the commercial rakers looking for whites are less likely to stumble on the black. There is also the Oregon brown truffle, as yet without a scientific name, which is said to be the equal of the black.

The challenge facing the Oregonian truffle trio is to become established in wider markets. High-quality truffles have to reach knowledgeable chefs and be turned into impressive dishes. Most chefs are trained in the classical French or Italian traditions, and if they learn anything at all about truffles, it is that the traditional European truffles are the best. Quality control at harvest time is obviously important, but with truffles being raked up unripe rather than sniffed out by dogs when at their best, this is very difficult. Raking produces good quantities of truffles that can be sold at a reasonable price. Using dogs might involve less physical work, but would probably reduce the numbers of truffles harvested. To make that worthwhile for the commercial collectors, the price of truffles would have to rise significantly. Given the huge price difference between the local truffles and imported European species, there's plenty of room to manoeuvre.

The Pacific Northwest may have the lion's share of the indige-

Oregon truffles can be found by hand (left), or more commonly, by raking.
(Charles Lefevre)

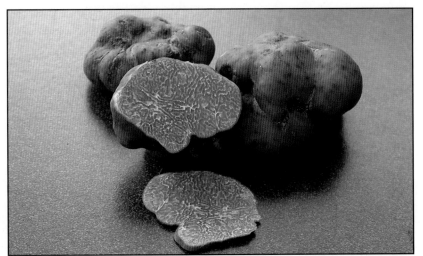

The pecan or Texas truffle, **Tuber lyonii,** *is found in pecan orchards in southeastern states, and can make very good eating.* (Charles Lefevre)

nous edible truffles, but in recent years another truffle, *Tuber lyonii,* known as the pecan or Texas truffle, has begun to make its mark in southeastern states. As the name suggests, it is commonly found in pecan orchards in Georgia, Florida, Texas and New Mexico, but it occurs naturally on other hosts over a huge area from New Mexico to the eastern seaboard and up to the Great Lakes and Canada. It's a smallish, brown truffle, not often larger than a golf ball, and can be found from August until November. When ripe it has a good aroma and flavour, but like all truffles can be disappointing when immature. In pecan orchards, growers often maintain a strip free of grass and weeds along the rows of trees, and pecan truffles can often be found just poking out of the soil surface. They are found either in this fashion or by raking, and can sometimes be found in great profusion. One hunter claims to have found almost ten kilos in two hours. They can be sold to enterprising restaurants for $200 per kilo. Their economic potential is obviously interesting, but with the harvesting methods used, getting hold of a really tasty truffle may be rather hit-and-miss – as with the Oregon truffles.

European truffles have none of the "image" problems of the indigenous American truffles, and though the quality of product reaching the US may be sometimes be questionable, there is a ready market in restaurants and upmarket food stores all over the country. Not surprisingly, there have been several attempts to set up truffières to capitalise on the demand. One of the first to get involved was Franklin Garland, of Hillsborough, North Carolina. In 1978 he came across a news item in the *Wall Street Journal* about French success in producing Périgord black truffles from specially inoculated trees. This struck him as an interesting opportunity, and in 1979 he planted his first seedling trees – 300 filberts (hazels) he'd attempted to infect with the Périgord black. After a decade of trial and error, he eventually produced his first truffles in 1991, and decided to plunge into the business full-time. His nursery now produces 20,000 trees per year, and many of them are being sold to local tobacco growers, whose livelihood has been threatened as smoking has become less popular. In 2004 he received a grant of $235,000 from the Tobacco Trust Fund Commission, a body set up by the state and funded with money from the settlement of legal action against the tobacco industry. Fifty local farmers were supplied with 200 free *Tuber melanosporum*-infected filberts in a bid to kick-start a local industry.

Pioneer US truffle grower and nurseryman Franklin Garland shows off h produce. (Alex Maness)

Garland is not on his own. In the mid-90s, a truffière of over 50,000 trees was planted in Hext, Texas, with backing from Urbani, one of Italy's biggest truffle traders. It's not doing well, I'm told, and may have been abandoned. There are also a couple of small but productive truffières in California, established with trees imported from France. One, near the Mendocino forest north of Ukiah in northern California, was established in 1980 and has been producing Périgord black truffles since the early 1990s. In winter 2004/5 it produced only a couple of pounds, but one of the truffles was "huge", according to the owner.

Hazels thriving in a productive five year-old truffière near Raleigh, Nort Carolina.v (Alex Mane

Interestingly, the trees for this site were kept in their pots for a year before being planted out, during which time truffles formed in the pots. This suggests that there could be a market niche for patio pots with truffle trees. You could grow your own truffles, perhaps even on an urban balcony!

In more recent times, Charles Lefevre, a mycologist who studied at the University of Oregon at Corvallis (where he learned his business from legendary truffle scientist Jim Trappe), has started a truffle-tree nursery. From its base at Eugene, Oregon, New World Truffières can supply a range of different trees infected with *melanosporum* and *uncinatum*, and he's trying to work out techniques for infecting young Douglas firs with *Tuber oregonense*. It is, he says, extremely difficult. Obviously one for a challenge, he's also trying to produce trees infected with the Italian white truffle, *Tuber magnatum*, and has a long waiting list for these despite warning all potential purchasers that they will "probably not succeed". In an article about his efforts in *Forbes* magazine in late 2004 he rather boldly speculated about the income that might be derived from a successful *magnatum* plantation: "If you could cultivate Italian whites," he said, "and if your trees managed to produce a hundred pounds per acre – which is common with French blacks – then at $2,000 a pound you'd make $200,000 per acre per year. If you had 10 acres, you could work leisurely for maybe five weeks each winter and have a $2 million annual income." The magazine's closing comment was "When truffle pigs fly." One of his customers now plans to call his *magnatum* plantation the Flying Pig Truffière. I look forward to flying over to pig out on its produce in due course.

There have been some efforts made to produce truffle-infected plants in Canada. A nursery called TrufAxiom was offering *Tuber melanosporum* infected plants in 2004, but has disappeared off the web recently. There may be some small parts of southern British Columbia that are warm enough for Périgord black truffles, and a wider area that could suit the Burgundy truffle, but the very cold winters could lead to truffles being frozen in the ground – if they did manage to fruit.

CHAPTER NINE

New Zealand & Australia

OBVIOUSLY I'M BIASED, but I think some of the most exciting things happening in the truffle business today are taking place in Australia and New Zealand. Neither country has any of the classic truffles of Europe growing in the wild (as far as we know), but both have keen growers with established truffières producing very high quality Périgord black truffles. In New Zealand, there are also trials under way with *Tuber uncinatum*, the Burgundy truffle, and *Tuber borchii*, the bianchetto of Italy.

The whole business was effectively started by one man, New Zealand mycologist Dr Ian Hall. In 1979 Hall was attending a conference at Fort Collins, Colorado.

"One day at lunch, I was sitting outside at an English-speaking table enjoying the company of old friends. Behind me was a French-speaking table. To describe my French as 'schoolboy standard' would be too kind, but during a lull in the conversation I heard someone behind me say that the first truffle from an artificial truffière had just been harvested. This piece of news registered with me, but no one said anything more and I thought no more about it for several months. Then one day it occurred to me that if they can do it in France, then surely we could do it in New Zealand too."

Cultivating black truffle in New Zealand wasn't as far-fetched an idea as it might seem. Parts of New Zealand have climates very similar to the regions of Europe where Périgord blacks are found, and there's no shortage of limestone and soils high in lime. Another advantage is that there is a marked lack of the competitive fungi that can invade European truffières. And if things worked, New Zealand truffles would be produced during the northern hemisphere summer, when there would be no fresh black truffles available in any of the world's major markets.

But there was one significant obstacle. New Zealand's strict agricultural quarantine regulations made importing infected trees from

Europe an impossibility. Any imported trees had to be quarantined and the roots disinfected, which would defeat the purpose of bringing them over in the first place. Hall had to find a means of infecting seedling trees in New Zealand with black truffle.

Shortly after he returned home, research on mycorrhizas in New Zealand fell victim to government spending cuts. It was not a good time to ask for money to grow truffles. But later the research climate warmed up again and in 1985 he decided to have a go at getting funding for truffle research. He wrote a 60-page proposal for "growing mushrooms on the roots of trees". "In the whole 60 pages I didn't mention mycorrhizas once," he told me. The tactic worked, and with $500 from the Ministry of Agriculture and $500 from a trust fund, he was able to get started. He didn't get much help from European scientists, but with "some luck and some careful science" he and his technician Sharon Roberts were able to produce a few dozen seedlings infected with Périgord black truffle. These were planted in two experimental truffières in north Otago, in the South Island, in 1987.

With interest in the idea of truffle-growing on the increase, the following year nine more truffières were planted in many different regions, from Gisborne on the east coast of the North Island to north Canterbury in the South Island. One of these was at Hall's brother Alan's property in Gisborne, and there, on 29 July 1993, the first Périgord black truffles grown in the southern hemisphere were harvested – only five years after planting. It was Ian Hall's birthday, and truffle was the only present he got from his brother that year. The first sign that there was anything in the ground was when the neighbour's pigs tried to break through

Alan Hall, the first person to harvest Périgord black truffles in the southern hemisphere, looks particularly pleased with one of the large truffles unearthed at an open day in June 1997.

Two truffles peep out of the ground at an amazingly productive truffière in the Bay of Plenty. Truffles can be so thick on the ground that it's impossible to walk through the trees without crushing truffles. (Ian Hall)

the fence to get into the truffière. Shortly after that first harvest, the pigs demolished the fence and polished off any truffles that may have been left. The truffière is now very securely fenced.

Over the next few years, Alan Hall's Oakland Truffière continued to produce small quantities of black truffle, but in 1997 he produced his first significant commercial harvest. By mid-June, his little half-hectare truffière had produced 6kg of truffles. At a field day held that month, in front of a crowd of interested growers and truffle scientists from around the world, he unearthed big truffle after big truffle. One enormous one weighed 750g and was worth over NZ$2,500. Another large one disappeared down the gullet of Tosca the doberman – a rather costly reward for her efforts on the day.

Since then, truffières have come into production in many regions, from the Bay of Plenty in the North Island, to Nelson and Canterbury in the South Island. Yields have ranged from small and scattered, to enormous and concentrated. At a tiny truffière in the Bay of Plenty, on a volcanic soil completely unlike any truffle terroir in Europe, the truffles form so close to the surface and in such profusion that it can be very difficult to walk through the trees without accidentally crushing them. Other truffières are more modest. The quality of the truffles is generally excellent, provided that they are harvested when fully ripe, but quantities available are small. They are snapped up by tourist lodges, embassies and knowledgeable restaurants, and the market price is stable at around NZ$3,500 per kilo, giving growers excellent returns. There has been keen interest from overseas, but there is simply not yet enough truffle to export – not when a typical export purchaser wants 100kg every week during the season.

There are now more than a hundred truffières around the country, and some large plantations are approaching the age when production should start. If all goes well, the harvest will increase considerably over the next few years, and exports will become a real possibility. Further large plantings are also likely, with investor interest from both within New Zealand and abroad. Growers have an active association, the NZ Truffle Association, to represent their interests and organise and fund research on their behalf.

The vast majority of truffle-infected trees are produced by Dr Hall's former employers, the government-owned research company Crop & Food Research Ltd, who are themselves involved in a number of truffière projects. Crop & Food Research's chief executive Paul Tocker believes that the industry will grow to become a $20 million export earner for New Zealand. Given the long lead time between planting a truffière and the start of production, it may take ten years or more for the industry to grow to that level, but there is no reason why it shouldn't do so. There are certainly plenty of keen growers willing to give it a go. Experiments with Burgundy truffle, which fruits in autumn, and bianchetto, a white truffle that fruits in late winter and early spring, could stretch the New Zealand truffle season to six months, and help establish a presence for the country in global markets.

Across the Tasman, Australia is blessed with a diverse and remarkable range of native truffle species, but little is known about their edibility. The aboriginal people certainly used many different kinds of edible fungi, including one that resembles the desert truffles that are so popular in North Africa and the Middle East, but nobody has yet discovered any local truffles that might stand comparison with the European and North American culinary species. Or perhaps none of the colonials have been brave enough to try them.

Efforts to grow Périgord black truffles in Australia began in the early 1990s. Prompted by the New Zealand experiments, Duncan Garvey and Peter Cooper from Tasmania discussed the possibility of truffle growing with Nick Malajczuk, a mycologist with an extensive knowledge of mycorrhizal fungi. In 1992 they founded Périgord Truffles of Tasmania (PTT) and set off for France to source truffles for their tree inoculation. They planted their first truffières in 1993 at Bream Creek and Bothwell in Tasmania, just as New Zealand was producing its first truffles at Gisborne. In contrast to the business in New Zealand, where growers buy trees

One of Tim Terry's Tasmanian truffières, planted with two kinds of oak trees: Quercus robur, the English oak, and Quercus ilex, the holly or holm oak.
(*Tim Terry*)

to plant on their own land, taking full responsibility for management of the truffière and the harvesting and marketing of truffles, PTT uses a different business model. Growers provide money, land and management, while PTT provides advice, trees, and marketing. Income from truffle sales is split between the partners. The new business was also given an early boost by generous tax breaks and research grants from state and federal governments keen to encourage agricultural diversification. As a result, interest developed quickly, and there are now at least 30 growers and more than 180 hectares of truffières in Tasmania, plus two more schemes of 30 hectares in the planning stages.

Other parts of Australia were also keen to get into the act. In the Margaret River region of Western Australia, widely known for the quality of its wines, Nick Malajczuk planted a 13,000-tree truffière at Manjimup in 1997. It's the largest truffière on the Australian mainland, and in recent years four more have been planted in the area. Truffières have also been planted in the Yarra valley and Goldfields region of Victoria, and in the southern highlands and several other parts of New South Wales. There are about 20 hectares in all, and plans to expand further.

Tasmania produced its first truffles on 18 June 1999, at Tim Terry's Askrigg property, not far from Launceston. Since then, truffles have been harvested on 11 other Tasmanian truffières, and in August 2003, Malajczuk's Manjimup plantation joined in, producing a palm-sized truffle. The following year, Manjimup produced over 100 truffles, but that still wasn't enough to satisfy local demand. Tasmanian production has not been huge, with most

Toasting the largest Périgord black truffle found outside France are (from left) Chef Alain Fabreques, Wally Edwards and Nick Malajczuk, owner of the Western Australian truffière where it was found in July 2005.
(Nick Malajczuk)

truffles being used by one Sydney restaurant. In the 2004 season, Western Australia produced around 10kg of truffles, and Tasmania slightly less, mainly because heavy rain in June left the ground waterlogged and the truffles rotted before they could be harvested. The 2005 season has been much better, with Nick Malajczuk finding a huge 1,018.5 g truffle in July – the largest ever found outside France (see above). Tasmanian growers have also done well.

The fledgling business has not been without its controversies. Shortly after harvesting Australia's first Périgord black, Tim Terry decided to enter the tree-production business himself, much to the annoyance of PTT, and has launched a couple of managed truffière schemes (totalling 12 hectares) at his Needlesdale property. New Zealand truffle growers were, perhaps understandably, upset when 'their' Crop & Food Research Ltd licensed its tree-infection technology to Raelene and Bill Stevenson of Australian Truffle Industries in Victoria. With at least four companies now competing for tree sales and investment dollars, there have been rather optimistic projections for truffle yields and income per hectare. There are tantalising hints from well-managed truffières in many parts of the world that truffle yields can sometimes be as high as 100kg per hectare – perhaps more. With southern hemisphere market prices stable at NZ$3,500 per kilo, that suggests an income potential of $350,000 per hectare - more than most forms of agriculture, even the illicit drug trade.

Unfortunately, however, those exciting production figures are not based on established agronomic data. If you want to plant a vineyard in Australia or New Zealand you can work with a century or more of local experience of costs, timings and yields. You might get your first grapes in year three, first commercial crop in year four, and be in full production in year five. Working in a big established market, you can accurately work out all your costs, and have a very good stab at what incomes you will generate. No one in Australia or New Zealand has that sort of data for truffles, and as a result the business still looks risky to many big investors. Only when both countries have got reliable and predictable figures for costs, timing of production and yields – not to mention an established marketing infrastructure – will the bigger investors feel comfortable. But that time will come.

Australia and New Zealand share many of the same challenges in bringing their truffle businesses to world markets, but competition is likely to be the least of their worries. Even if every truffière in both countries produced record yields of truffles this year, they would still fall well short of satisfying the world demand. The issue is one of managing scarcity, rather than finding markets. It will be decades before southern hemisphere production approaches anywhere near current in-season northern hemisphere production, and the south will always have the advantage of producing outside the northern season. Even with that advantage, quality will have to be paramount. If a truffle is sold for a high price and air-freighted to a top restaurant in London, it will have to be in perfect condition when it gets there. One bad truffle sent to one top chef could be a marketing disaster. I may have to deliver mine by hand.

Hazels flourishing in Nick Malajczuk's Manjimup truffière
(Nick Malajczuk)

CHAPTER TEN
China & Asia

THE CHINESE love mushrooms. They use hundreds of different kinds as food and medicine. They export vast quantities of fungi all round the world, including tonnes of truffles - truffles that have taken the world market by storm because they're cheap, and

look a lot like real Périgord blacks - even though their aroma and flavour is a lot less intense.

Chinese truffles are usually called *Tuber indicum* in Europe, but the black truffles found in China include *Tuber pseudoexcavatum*, *Tuber indicum*, *Tuber sinense*, *Tuber himalayense* and *Tuber pseudohimalayense*. A final determination of names remains to be made. They ripen over winter, from November to March. A summer white truffle is also exported, but this has not been given a scientific name at the time of writing. The centre of the truffle business is in the provinces of Yunnan and Sichuan in the southwest, on the border with Tibet. They account for 95 percent of Chinese truffle exports, and Yunnan is the biggest single producer.

The resemblance that Chinese black truffle species bear to *Tuber melanosporum* is striking. The skin can be the same warty black colour and the flesh is similarly marbled and coloured. The aroma and flavour are, however, much less intense

Chinese truffles are available for around US$50 per kilo, and by the sackful.
(Yu Fuqiang)

Typical Chinese truffle forest: **Pinus yunnanensis** *growing in the red soils characteristic of many Chinese truffl？regions.* (Yu Fuqiang)

than *melanosporum*. Some people report that they taste slightly bitter, though that's not universal. If *himalayensis* truffles weren't such a dark colour, you could call them a "pale imitation" of the real thing, but they are perfect candidates for passing off. The only major difference between the two species is that the flesh of *indicum* is not as firm as that of *melanosporum*. It has been compared to the difference between emmental cheese, which is slightly rubbery and flexible, and parmesan, which is harder and more crumbly.

Although there have been reports in western media that the Chinese don't like eating eat their own truffles, Chinese black truffles have been collected, eaten and traded by the local population for a very long time. They are regarded as a delicacy, perhaps even a health food. They can be served with chicken in a hotpot dish, or on their own, lightly fried in peanut oil. The Chinese also make the world's only truffle wine, a strong and pungent brew. The export trade that has developed in the last ten years has made truffles an important part of the regional economy. The farmers who make money by digging up the warty black balls find it difficult to believe they're in such demand in the west.

Chinese black truffle species grow in association with a range of host plants in the Pinaceae and Fagaceae, notably *Pinus yunnanensis*, *Pinus armandii*, *Keteleeria evelyniana* and *Quercus* species. They are harvested by raking and digging. Unfortunately, as with the white truffles of Oregon, this leads to quality and environmental problems, as many immature truffles are harvested alongside mature

ones. Perhaps therein lies one of the reasons that
Chinese truffles have such a poor reputation. But
whatever the quality, production is enormous. One
single exporter claims to be able to ship up to 20
tonnes of black truffle in a season, equal to the
entire French harvest in a moderate year.

Until the early 1990s, Chinese truffles were virtually unknown in the west, but as the Chinese
economy liberalised, the seemingly inexorable
drop in European truffle production and soaring
prices stimulated an interest in this cheap alternative. Initially, exports to Europe were sporadic, but in the winter
of 1994–95 some experts believe that Chinese truffle imports were
twice the French production of *melanosporum*. There was wide-
spread fraud, because many found it hard to resist the temptation
to buy a look-alike truffle for a few hundred francs a kilo and sell
it for a few thousand. And if the aroma wasn't particularly strong,
then that could be fixed with a few drops of truffle oil or some
hours in a bag with a ripe example of the real thing.

*Truffle wine is a
popular and strong
drink, here accom-
panying a mush-
room stir-fry.*
(Yu Fuqiang)

Since that initial underhand storming of the market (which was
certainly not the fault of the Chinese), the Chinese truffle has
become a part of the worldwide truffle market. There is still a lot
of discreet "upgrading" of imports to Europe, but this should be
getting rarer thanks to consumer legislation requiring truffles to be
labelled with their origin, together with new DNA tests to distinguish quickly between species. *Tuber indicum* is now sold worldwide,
both fresh and preserved, correctly labelled – most of the time.
It is a cheap alternative to the real thing, but as with the summer
truffle, *Tuber aestivum*, there is a risk that some restaurants and
consumers might think that a truffle is a truffle, buy some *indicum*
(or *aestivum*, or *brumale* for that matter) and then wonder what all
the fuss is about. The only solution to that problem is education,
a close reading of product labels, and experience with good ripe
black and white truffles.

Tuber indicum has been found in Japan, and a very similar new species, *Tuber formosanum*, has recently been recorded in Taiwan. *Tuber
aestivum* (also known as *Tuber uncinatum*, the Burgundy truffle) has
been recently recorded in China. With economic forces driving
new interest in China's truffles, more new records or new species
of truffles are likely to be discovered.

CHAPTER ELEVEN
Sweden & the rest of the world

IF YOU WERE GOING to pick the perfect place in Europe to start a new truffle cultivation business, you probably wouldn't pick the middle of the Baltic Sea. But there, on Gotland, an island 90 km off the Swedish coast, attempts are being made to grow the Burgundy truffle, *Tuber aestivum* (also known as *Tuber uncinatum*). Gotland was the only place in Sweden

known to have *aestivum* occurring naturally, but until the late 1990s it was only known from three sites. However, in 1997 Christina Wedén, a student mycologist working on her master's thesis, was asked by her supervisor, Eric Danell, to see what she could find. She quickly added a fourth site to the list, and found a 225g truf-

Hunting Burgundy truffle in Swedish truffle country - hazel woodland.
(Christina Wedén)

Tuber aestivum truffière on Gotland. (*Christina Wedén*)

fle – a Swedish record. In 1998 she made further good finds, and over the next two years explored the island with the aid of French-trained truffle dogs, adding another 27 sites to the list.

Gotland is clearly a good place to grow Burgundy truffle. Although it has cold winters, the surrounding sea moderates the worst of the winter freeze, summers are warm, and autumns are long and mild. The natural oak-and-hazel woodlands and high-pH soils suit *aestivum* very well. But there is some mystery about how the truffle got there, because Gotland didn't emerge from the Baltic until the end of the last ice age, about 11,000 years ago, and hasn't been linked to either Sweden or Estonia since. Truffles rely on animals to distribute their spores, but unless Estonian squirrels are very strong swimmers, or skied over the ice on one of the rare occasions when the Baltic froze over that far South, there has to have been some other vector. Insects are the obvious candidate, and Wedén found evidence that beetles and other insects could carry truffle spores in their gut. A wind-blown beetle could have delivered truffle spores from Sweden.

In 1999, Wedén and local landown-ers began some trial plantations of trees inoculated with *aestivum*. Ten truffières of 24 trees (12 oaks and 12 hazels, sourced from France) were planted in suitable loca-tions. The following year, a further 3,000 oaks were planted, and by 2005 there were

Christina Wedén plants one of the first artifically inoculated plants. (*Christina Wedén*)

25 truffières and at least 2,500 trees approaching production age. Investigating the roots shows that *aestivum* is doing well, but at the time of writing no plantations had yet produced truffles. The trees are still young, though, and hopes are high. And in my trial plot of *uncinatum/aestivum* trees, I have some infected with Swedish truffles, thanks to Christina. One day I hope she will be able to enjoy eating some New Zealand-grown Swedish Burgundy truffle.

Tuber aestivum grows naturally over a wide area of Europe, from North Africa to Sweden, and from Britain to Russia. In many places it has been collected and eaten, especially in countries which enjoy fungi rather more than Britain. Other truffles, such as *Tuber borchii* and *Tuber mesentericum*, the Bagnoli truffle, are also distributed throughout much of Europe, and do get eaten from time, but haven't formed the basis of a substantial business.

Beyond the new truffle-growing activities in North America, New Zealand and Australia, South Americans have also been showing an interest. Chile and Argentina both have regions where the climatic requirements of the Périgord black can easily be met, and as their wine industries have shown, they are not afraid of investing in large plantings and modern techniques. In South Africa, at least one farmer has been experimenting with the Périgord black, having imported inoculated trees from Franklin Garland in the USA. If both continents prove conducive to truffle growing, then southern hemisphere production could, in a decade or two, get a real boost.

Truffles and truffle-like fungi have been used by cultures all round the world, and not just for food. In Mexico, truffles called el gran mundo ('the big world' – *Elaphomyces granulatus* and related species) were used as the centrepiece of ceremonies that involved the participants taking so-called magic (hallucinogenic) mushrooms. The Japanese adore many kinds of mushrooms, particularly a truffle-like species called *Rhizopogon rubescens*, known as shoro. It doesn't have pronounced flavour, but is much esteemed for its mouthfeel and is an important ingredient in a special soup. There are reports from early settlers in New Zealand that the Maori sometimes dug up and ate a truffle-like fungus, but it isn't clear what that might have been, and the habit has long been lost. Across the Himalayas from the hyperactive Chinese truffle business, there are reports of truffles being harvested and eaten in Nepal, probably where the name *Tuber indicum* originally came from, but no exploitation on an international basis. Pakistan and India both export large quantities of morels, a very tasty spring mushroom, but do yet not appear to have latched on to the truffles that are probably in their mountain forests.

CHAPTER TWELVE

Truffle Hunting

MY NOSE IS NOT UP TO THE TASK of finding truffles, and nor is yours, however large it may be. At human nose height, the aroma just isn't strong enough to let us home in on where the things are lurking. If I put my nose to the ground, and I'm close to a fully ripe truffle that has filled the soil around it with powerful odorants, then I'll notice something. If I stick my nose into the hole, then I will be overwhelmed, even after that fully ripe truffle has been removed. I could, if I had knees and a back that could take the strain, not to mention a lot of time, quarter the truffière on my hands and knees, nose to ground, until I found a truffle. On balance though, I think I'd rather leave that job to our amazingly charming truffle hound, Peg.

There are other ways of finding truffles. If you can master the techniques, and have a good eye for the right location, then you may have considerable success without a dog. In shallow soils, and if conditions are right, a truffle can form just under the soil surface and as it enlarges in late summer and early autumn, it may give a

Sometimes a truffle can break the surface; this one (in Hugues Martin's truffière) has been attacked by insects.

fairly clear hint of its presence. You might see the warty black top emerging from the ground, a tell-tale crack in the soil surface, or even a sort of volcanic-looking mound. This can be surprisingly obvious in Périgord black truffle truffières, where the fungus suppresses weed growth around the tree, but is less helpful with other truffles when the trees are surrounded with plants.

Digging and raking is certainly a viable technique. All Oregon white truffles that come to market over autumn and winter are harvested by raking. The Victorian amateur naturalists, who did a lot of the seminal science on truffles in England, used little hand-rakes. One of New Zealand's truffle scientists is seldom seen without her rake, and she's found the first truffles in many of our productive truffières.

This is what you do. Find a likely-looking tree. Drop to your knees and start raking a few inches away from the base of the trunk. Gradually excavate a triangular segment of soil, keeping an eye open for truffles. When you start hitting tree roots, you won't be able to go any deeper. If there's nothing there, replace the soil and move on to another segment. The advantage of this method is obvious: if there's anything there in the top layers, then you'll find it. The drawbacks are equally clear: you won't find any truffle that's too deep for your rake (and in deep soils they can grow 50cm or more below the surface), and you will find truffles that aren't ripe. As we saw when looking at Oregon white truffles, collecting unripe truffles has given them an unjustly poor reputation. A similar thing may be going on with Chinese truffles, which are also harvested with rakes.

In the past, keen French peasants (and at least one gung-ho New Zealand grower) have used spades and shovels to try to dig up truf-

Tell-tale cracks in the Tasmanian soil announce the presence of a truffle swelling beneath the surface. (Tim Terry)

fles. It's hard work, hit-and-miss, and does too much
damage to the tree roots and the fungus. It's not
advised, and not much practised today.

A much more restful and non-invasive way of
finding truffles is by the fly, or *à la mouche* as the
French put it. Gustaf Sobin's poetic little novel *The
Fly Truffler*, has a very good description of the technique as used in Provence:

*A fungal treasure
house: a "nest" of
Chinese truffles.*
(*Yu Fuqiang*)

"With the oak woods on one side, the abandoned
almond orchards on the other, Cabassac held the sun
fixed like a compass point directly before him. That
way, he knew, he wouldn't be casting a shadow over the brittle winter
grasses: the very haunt of those tiny, strawlike insects. Wouldn't be
disturbing those diptera until the very last second. Because it was their
sudden, spasmodic flight that betrayed their secret. They'd spring rather
than fly, revealing as they did the exact point over which they'd just
perched. It was there, in the heavily scented earth directly beneath, that
they'd lay their eggs. There too, but at a depth of ten, twenty, even thirty
centimetres, that – by a miracle of pure symbiosis – one of those black,
odoriferous tubers could be found. One of those coveted truffles, firmly
cradled in the very earth it so richly embalmed."

There are several species of truffle fly (*Suillia gigantea*, *Helomyza
tuberivora* and *Helomyza lineata* are the most important), but they
all do the same thing. They lay their eggs in the soil above the truffle, and when the larvae hatch they feast on the fruit body. As the
truffles ripen towards maturity, the flies gather in swarms, as do the
truffle hunters.

To hunt for truffles *à la mouche*, you must first find a branch
off a pine tree. In Provence this would be the Aleppo pine, *Pinus
halapensis*. Strip off all the side branches until you have only a little plume of needles at the end. Then find a likely looking brulée,
and sweep your brush gently through the vegetation or across the
soil surface. If you are lucky, you will disturb a fly. It will take off
with a little jump, or at least "a marked lack of grace", according to
Provençal rabassier Jean-Marie Rocchia. Carefully mark the spot,
and then sniff the soil surface. If the fly was doing its job properly,
you should smell truffle. All you have to do is to carefully dig it up.
If you're really lucky, you may find what Rocchia calls a "nest" of
truffles – a group of truffles growing together.

This is a method that requires good eyesight, a good nose, and
patience. Compared with random raking, it has the obvious advantage that it finds ripe, aromatic truffles – but it doesn't guarantee
that you will find only *Tuber melanosporum*. You could just as easily

unearth a *brumale, mesentericum* or *uncinatum*. Nor is it quick. French truffle hunters may spend hours watching a good brulée, waiting for the flies to gather over the truffle they suspect to be there. In some countries, for example New Zealand, there are no truffle flies, or none that we know of, so fly-truffling is out.

A slightly more off-beam method of truffling has been sweeping through Europe in the last few years: dowsing. Respectable truffle hunters, and even a truffle scientist of some renown (who shall remain nameless), believe they can find truffles by walking around with a couple of pieces of bent wire in their hands, or that with the aid of a pendulum they can tell whether truffle-infected seedlings have got the right fungus on their roots. Should you want to give dowsing a go, this is how you do it. Cut two pieces of fence wire each about 50 cm and bend 20-cm "handles". Grip the handles in your fists quite loosely and hold the wires so that the long bits are roughly parallel to the ground and each other. They

Dowsing for truffle in Italy. When the wires cross, you are supposed to be stand-ing over a truffle (probably).

should be free to move. Get someone to hide a truffle somewhere, then with your hands at stomach level, slowly walk around concentrating on the wires. If your dowsing technique is good, if the signals (whatever they may be) are getting through, then the wires will twitch and cross as you move over the truffle. Or they will if you know what you're doing. I don't. Nor, in the opinion of the vast majority of scientists in this field, do the dowsers. Still, some people swear by it – though I doubt they've got rid of their dogs.

Hunting truffles in the wild in France and Italy is not a simple business. There are extensive rules and regulations regarding the dates that each species of truffle can be harvested and sold. In

Italy, anyone who wishes to look for truffles has to sit an exam
and obtain a license before being allowed out with their dog. They
aren't allowed to look at night, either. France is less regulated, and
caveurs, as truffle hunters are called, can go anywhere where they
have rights of access, or have permission to visit. If you're lucky
enough to own a home in the Luberon or Umbria, and it has some
woodland on it, then you will almost certainly find a local who
will be willing to pay you in truffle for the chance to have a sniff
around. I'd rather have my own dog, and keep all the truffles, but
I'd probably be ostracised and driven out of the village for denying
someone his living.

   Every truffle hunter has his personal mental map of the good
spots, and will return to them throughout the season and from
year to year. The prime sites will have been handed down from one
generation to the next, and will probably be a jealously guarded
secret. I certainly don't share my best mushrooming sites with
anyone I suspect might like the things as much as I do. The canny
truffle hunter will adopt a circuitous route to his site, to throw
potential competitors off the track. In Italy, unscrupulous hunters have been known to leave bits of poisoned meat or other
tasty morsels lying around in prime spots, to kill off other hunters' dogs and thus reduce competition. Indeed, during my visit to
Italy doing the research for this book the problem had become
so pressing that many hunters had taken to working their dogs
on leads. And of course, the high prices commanded by truffles
mean that they are a very tempting proposition for poachers. At
a truffière I visited in the Périgord, the owner cheerfully admitted that he would often spend the night in an old stone shepherd's
hut (a gariotte, see p. 37), shotgun by his side, keeping watch over
his truffles. If poachers dared to trespass in his trees, he fired
a parachute flare up into the sky, and its glaring light gave him
the chance to get a few shots off. Not a man to cross, obviously,
but a few shotgun pellets in the seat of your pants would be a
small price compared to that paid by trespassers in one Italian
wood, where the owner laid land mines to protect his crop.

   When you're looking for truffles, it pays to understand the sites
and the sorts of trees they grow best with. The Périgord black
grows best in open oak woodland with limestone soils, and often
(but not always) advertises its presence with a brulée. Searching
for *Tuber magnatum* is a different proposition. The Italian white
lives in deep humid soils, in valley bottoms. It grows under limes,
poplars and willows as well as oaks. It produces no brulée, and productive sites are often thickets that have to be penetrated, rather

than woods to walk through. The truffles are often found at greater depths than *melanosporum*, and the Italian truffle hunter will have a range of different tools to help dig them up. The commonest is a sort of long-handled, narrow trowel. A French truffle hunter, looking in his stony soils, might also use a trowel, albeit one with a shorter handle, and a screwdriver might help to shift rocks and stones.

*A fine collection of tools (and random deer skull) used for excavating **Tuber magnatum** at the home of renowned Bologna tartufaio Lucio Pierantoni.*

Of all the methods used to find truffles, my favourite is the technique used by a woman in the North Island of New Zealand. She can find them by walking over the surface of the ground in bare feet. She feels the slight difference in the soil texture where there's one under the surface. Then she falls to her knees, assesses the smell, and harvests the truffle. The method only works in truffières where the soil is just right, but the sight of this lady in action has amazed more than one world-leading truffle researcher. In winter, getting around in bare feet on frosty ground has to present an extra challenge. One wonders whether the technique would work through thick socks.

Flies, rakes and feet all have their merits and their devotees, but only one system really works for commercial harvesting of large quantities of ripe truffle. And it barks.

CHAPTER THIRTEEN
Dogs and Pigs
(but mainly Dogs)

A DOG IS A WONDERFUL PIECE of biomechanical engineering. At the front end of a mobile platform capable of sophisticated movement and enthusiastic digging there is an aroma-detector of great sensitivity. The two are tied together by a biological computer sophisticated enough to learn to work by command. The only inputs required are raw meaty bones, some small rewards for successful execution of the desired tasks, and a lot of tender loving care. And a dog loves you back. You don't get that from a machine.

Truffle-sniffing machines can certainly be built. A working one was demonstrated by a Yorkshireman, John Sonley, in the early 1990s, but no manufacturer could be found to commercialise the product. Gas-detection technology has moved on a lot since then, but the commercial realities haven't changed. The market for truffle sniffers around the world is not large, but dogs are plentiful and (relatively) cheap. They are also, dare I say it, more fun.

A dog's nose is said to be somewhere between ten thousand and a million times more sensitive than a human's. Experiments in the US to examine the effectiveness of dogs as explosives sniffers have shown that they have no difficulty sniffing out certain chemicals at concentrations as low as 10 parts per billion. Our beagle Peg has relatives who work at Auckland airport, sniffing bags as people arrive – not for drugs, but for food items that are not allowed into the country. I'm told that they can smell an orange in someone's bag at 30 metres – sometimes even after the orange was removed hours earlier.

Peg is *ruled* by her nose. She sniffs everything, sucking air over her complicated little nasal passages, making loud snuffling noises when she's working hard, building up a scent picture of the world. She will sometimes put her nose to the crack round the door and noisily sniff up a huge lungful of air to try and figure out what's happening outside. Smell means more to her than vision: I've

watched her chasing a rabbit trail, nose to the ground, ears flying, while the rabbit runs in the opposite direction only metres away. Her concentration on what her nose is telling her is almost fierce.

Pigs are a feasible biomechanical alternative to dogs, and were widely used as truffle finders in the days when most rural homes kept a pig or two. They have good noses, love digging, and their love of truffles is innate, so they require no training. Wild pigs like nothing more than to destroy pasture by rooting through it for things to eat. It's an impressive sight, the devastation wrought by a few pigs on a paddock.

To find a good truffling pig, all you have to do is visit a pig farmer when he's got a few piglets. Stuff a truffle in your pocket, and buy the piglet that shows the most interest. Then all you need is a lead. Let the pig find a truffle, but pull it away before it can eat it. Give it something to eat (they'll eat anything), and pocket the truffle for yourself. Simple, at least when the pig is small. When the pig is a mature sow, it's not so easy. Have you ever tried to pull a mature sow away from its favourite delicacy? No, neither have I. Mature sows aren't small, have stubborn minds of their own, and won't fit into the back of a small car. A couple of years ago, we tried to see if a neighbour's pet pig would be any use as a truffle-finder. We couldn't even persuade it to get onto a trailer for the short journey, despite offerings of food it normally considered delicious. Dogs are much more tractable. Peg, for instance, can simply be picked up under one arm and transported wherever I wish. And she'll fit in the back of the car, though being

New Zealand truffle pig in festive mood. As yet unproven as a truffle finder.
(Pat Nelson)

the champion she is, she has taken to jumping up onto the front passenger seat and looking most affronted when you turf her out. Pigs don't do that, for which you might be grateful.

Studies of dog DNA suggests that dogs have been living and working with humans for around 90,000 years, when something very like a grey wolf must have been domesticated. At first there seem to have been no distinct breeds, but around 15,000 years ago, some of the differences we see between breeds began to emerge. Skill with the nose would have been inherited from their wolf forebears, but the early breeders would have been keen to keep or improve the faculty. It's not a very big jump from finding and tracking prey (or enemies), to dogs specialised as fetchers and retrievers.

There are two breeds of dog that are traditionally associated with truffle hunting, and both were designed to be water retrievers. To do their job of retrieving game from lakes and marshes, they have to be able to scent the target animal – a dead duck, perhaps – at considerable distances over water. Nose in the air, in other words. That's how I tell when Peg is doing her job properly. If she's sniffing the ground, she's tracking rabbits or other animals, but if her head's up sniffing, I know (or hope) she's looking for truffles.

The Italian lagotto romagnolo is the only breed defined as a truffle hunter, and it started out as a duck retriever in the marshes of north-east Italy. After those marshes were drained in the late nineteenth century, the dogs were put to a new use. One of their particular advantages, apart from a fine nose, is that all urge to chase game has been bred out of them. This is not true of beagles,

Sweden's top truffle dogs resting after a hard day's sniff. Christina Wedén's springer spaniel Biscuit, with colleagues Alice (labrador) and lagotto romagnolo Lizzy.
(Christina Wedén)

sadly. Lagottos remind me of a cross between a terrier and a poodle, which is perhaps not surprising when one Italian expert has said that the breed's nearest equivalent is the Irish water terrier, and that poodles were originally bred as water retrievers.

Poodles are, in fact, the other breed strongly associated with truffle hunting. They've been used that way for hundreds of years. In 1746, a German authority on the breed claimed that poodles were the best of all dogs for truffle hunting, and they were widely employed in France, Italy and Spain, as well as the parts of Germany where truffles can be found.

But that's not the last word on truffle dogs. French author Jean-Marie Rocchia waxes lyrical in his appreciation of the powers of the dachshund: "From chihuahua to Saint Bernard, all breeds of dog can be trained to find truffles, and you only have to help out at a truffle dog trial to find that out. Nevertheless, one can affirm that there are two groups of dogs suitable for truffle hunting: dachshunds, which are excellent, and all other dogs, amongst which you may find some that are very good." One of their many advantages, he avers, is their short legs, which keep them close to the truffles.

Pit-bull pups preparing for a life looking for buried treasure — and then protecting it against all comers

Other experts would have you believe that labradors are the only choice, and others swear by German shepherds. An Italian bloke I met on my travels insisted that the pit-bull puppies he was training would be excellent. "They will find truffles, yes," he said, "and then they will make sure that no one else gets them!" The last word on breeds, however, must go to Italian scientist Alessandra Zambonelli, who once advised NZ Truffle Association members that the best breed used in Italy was the bastardo. "I've never heard of that before," said one member. Alessandra smiled faintly, and looked around for help. "It means the dog doesn't know who his father is," she offered. In other words, your common and garden mongrel. There is, apparently, a lot to be said for hybrid vigour.

When you meet a truffle grower or hunter, it doesn't take long for the conversation to turn to dogs. Your choice of breed (or half-breed) is only one potential topic. There are many others. How do you train your dog? What's the best reward? How long will the dog work for at a time? Does it concentrate on its job or chase rabbits? This is unsentimental interest, not some pet-lover's ooh-ing and aah-ing about their overfed pooch. If a truffle dog isn't working well, the owner is losing money. One missed truffle that rots in the ground is hundreds of dollars or euros of lost income. We exchange this information because it's important.

There are controversies too. Some people insist that dogs work best when rewarded with little cubes of cheese, while others insist that cheese ruins their noses, and that little bits of sausage or meaty treats are the only effective reward. Professional trainers often suggest that dogs should be rewarded by being allowed to play with a favourite toy – but that only attracts scorn from the French. These are subjects that are not open to rational resolution, and their convoluted exploration excites trufficulteurs in much the same way as the weather endlessly fascinates the British (and me).

So what follows is my particular perspective on truffle dogs and their training. It is not the last word on dogs, and there will be many dog experts and truffle hunters who will disagree, perhaps violently, with what I have to say. Nevertheless, Peg was the first-ever champion truffle hound in New Zealand, so the two of us know *something*, at least. Obviously I believe that beagles make wonderful truffle hounds (though it's still too early in Peg's career for me to say exactly *how* wonderful), but I think the question of breed is secondary to having a dog that you can work with, that fits in with your circumstances – and your family. I would also suggest that you should, if at all possible, get your dog as a young puppy – around eight to twelve weeks old or as soon as the breeder is pre-pared to let you have it. Some experts suggest that you should work with a dog of the opposite sex, and I can't quarrel with that. Others would suggest that you visit the litter with a truffle in your pocket and pick the puppy that shows the most interest in the smell. I didn't have any truffle, and it didn't seem to matter.

When you get the puppy home, keep it with you as much as pos-sible. From the day she arrived, Peg accompanied me from farm to office, where she spent the day in a little fold-up metal pen. Every now and again I would pick her up and give her some attention, then return her to the pen. It's all about forming a bond, and Peg and I managed that very easily. The puppy also has to find its place in the pack that already live at its new home: that's at the bottom of the family heap. In our house, the heap includes the cats. There are various ways of ensuring that the dog knows its place, as it were, and they are very simple and effective. There's plenty of general dog-training material around, but I recommend the works of Jan Fennel, the "dog listener", who, inspired by horse whisperers, has developed some effective techniques for controlling dog behaviour.

Peg's training started more or less straight away, and the principles I used are exactly the same as those suggested by that 18th century poodle expert. At three months or so, we started playing with truffle-scented baits. I used plastic film canisters, into which I placed some cotton wool and a few drops of truffle oil. With holes pierced in the soft lid, these are ideal for hiding around the place. In 1746, they used a leather pouch with a bit of truffle sewn inside, and in Italy today, some lagotto trainers use a ball of rags tied together and scented with truffle oil, called a strufiòn. In France, you can buy a specially formulated dog-training truffle fluid in little tins. Canitruff, it's called. If you have spare truffle to hand, you can use that. It is possible to buy "training grade" truffles in season (and, frozen, out of season in some places), and these work perfectly. I keep several ready-made real truffle baits in the freezer and bring them out when I need them. After they've been buried for an hour or two there's no shortage of scent for the dog to find. I also believe that real truffle is easier for a dog to find than truffle oil, so there may be a case for training a dog on oil to make it easier to find the real thing. In any event, I reckon that dogs think finding truffles is easy – and training them to do it is not hard. Getting them to *work* hard, however, is quite another matter.

The first phase of training is to introduce the puppy to the smell. Then you start playing hide-and-seek with the baits. Put them down on the floor, and when the puppy goes over and sniffs the bait, reward it with a treat. We use little bits of a commercially available sort of beef jerky for dogs. Easy to handle, not at all messy,

This Provençal rabassier clearly knows how to make his dog work for him
(Andy Mikkelsen)

and very popular with Peg. As the puppy gets the idea, gradually start to hide the baits around the room – behind curtains, under chairs and so on – and be very effusive with your praise and generous with your rewards whenever it finds them. Peg only took about ten minutes to get the idea, and then it was simply a question of making her nose do more and more work. We hid the baits around the house while the puppy was in another room, and then let her find them. And when she'd mastered that (another ten minutes), we could move outside, hiding the baits around the garden.

After a week or two of garden searches, I began to bury the baits just under the surface of the soil, and encouraged her to scratch to find them. The idea here is to get the dog to mark the spot where the truffle is, enabling you to dig it up, rather than trying to dig it up by herself. Although dogs aren't mad about truffles, they will eat them if given a chance.

Peg had no problem finding the buried baits. So we buried them a bit deeper. Still no problem. The next stage was to introduce her to the truffière. I buried the baits around the trees, waited a while for the smell to permeate the soil, and then began to establish a little ritual. I started to work her on a lead, to keep her from getting sidetracked chasing after rabbits. As a result, nowadays putting the lead on, together with taking a trowel from the garage and stuffing some beef strips into my pocket is a pretty clear signal to Peg that we're off to do some work. She gets almost pathetically excited at the prospect, bouncing from paw to paw and eager to lead me to the trees.

The transition to the truffière went well. It was obvious, though, that although she loved the game, she was following my scent trail to the places where I'd buried the baits. So I began a devious process of criss-crossing the truffière as I laid the baits, hoping to lay down a confusion of scents. It didn't seem to make much difference: Peg still found them all with ease. So I cajoled other family members into helping out, or adopted a tactic used by other trainers: throwing baits a few metres away while riding round the truffière on a farm bike. Still no problem. I was confident that we'd done as much as we could in basic training, and the next stage would have to involve real truffles.

Therein lay a dilemma. In Europe, a truffle dog can learn its trade and then go to places where truffles occur naturally, or to well-established truffières, in the expectation that there will be real ones to find. The dog may also be able to work with some established dogs, to learn from its peers. This is not so easy when black truffles don't occur in the wild, and your own truffière is not yet

Alessandra Zambonelli's dog Tuberina hard at work.

producing truffles. Peg could find truffle baits, but could she find real truffles?

She could. We took her round to a nearby truffière that had just begun production, and she found truffles. Nice ripe Périgord black truffles. Her reward was a perfect little truffle, and I don't know who was more excited – the dog or I. She was, I suspect, greatly relieved when I swapped the truffle for a large bone. Now all she has to do is find them at home.

I said earlier that I thought that dogs think finding truffles is easy. My neighbour got his first truffles while doing a bit of puppy training. He was introducing the dog to the truffière, and it was doing well. Then they noticed that it was scratching around trees where they hadn't planted baits. In went a trowel, and out came a truffle. Great excitement!

Peg and I are now learning our trade together. Having a dog that can find truffles is one thing, but having one that can find them *commercially* is quite another. The first NZ Truffle Association dog trial proved the point. Peg won, by being fastest to find all the baits, but the only dog there that was a proven, commercial truffle finder didn't do so well. What's more important, the prize or the truffle? I'll take the truffle, thanks.

There are a number of ground rules (or old wives' tales, depending on your perspective) that I apply when looking for truffles. The best time to work the dog is in the morning, preferably a dry morning with not much wind. A strong wind will blow any truffle smell away, and waterlogged soil will not release the aroma as freely as dry soil will. Don't feed the dog before heading out for work; in fact some would suggest not feeding it the night before, but I'm not that tough. You should start downwind of the trees, so that the smell is blown towards the dog and it can then track the smell back to its source. Don't try and work the dog for too long. They all have their natural attention spans. Don't lose your temper if the dog's not working. You need to get it working to please you and to get the treat – not because it's frightened of you.

Every year, as summer advances, I remind Peg about her job by gradually stepping up her work with baits. By the time winter's here, I'm working her two or three times a week, and during the truffle season, I will work her in my truffière at least twice a week. Will this year be the one where she finds our first truffle? We live in hope.

If you get all that right, then you have a valuable beast. Every year, horror stories emerge from Europe about dogs being stolen or poisoned. In the Vaucluse in southern France a couple of years ago, a champion truffle hound worth at least 3,000 euro was stolen – part of a rash of dog thefts in that region. The dog, a seven-year-old black mongrel called Julie, but better known by her nickname la pelleteuse (the mechanical digger), was a celebrity in truffle circles around Uzes, and the thieves took her while ignoring her less-fêted kennel mates. In Italy, because the valuable *Tuber magnatum* is only found in the wild, some unscrupulous tartufaio have taken to leaving poisoned bits of meat around in prime spots, presumably hoping to knock out the competition. None of that has reached New Zealand yet, and I hope it never does.

CHAPTER FOURTEEN
The Truffle Business

GETTING A TRUFFLE FROM TERROIR TO TABLE is not a trivial undertaking. A fresh truffle from Périgord or Piedmont might end up on a restaurant plate in any of the world's cities, but with a shelf life of only a week to 10 days, it has to get there fast. During the great French truffle boom at the end of the 19th century, fresh truffles could be shipped around Europe by rail, and there was a reasonable chance that they would get to the customer in good condition, but the rest of the world could only eat canned or bottled truffle. Large factories were established to preserve truffles, and the owners became very influential. They bought fresh truffle in the village and town markets, and acted as wholesalers and distributors of truffles, as well as keeping their bottling and canning lines busy. In principle, the market still works the same way, though there has been a huge decline in both truffle production and numbers of people involved in it.

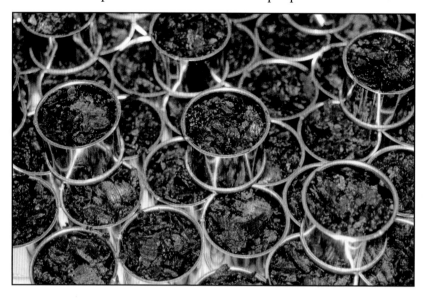

Preserved truffle pieces in the process of being canned at the Pébeyre head office in Cahors.

French truffle markets are as various as the towns they're held in. Each has its own rules, regulations, and style of doing business. At Lalbenque, near Cahors, the market opens every Tuesday afternoon during the season. The truffle growers and hunters line the street with their wares displayed in front of them. The buyers walk up and down, inspecting what's being offered. At 2:30 sharp a whistle is blown, and the buyers approach the sellers and give them a slip of paper showing the quantity they're prepared to buy and the price they're willing to pay. At the end of the market, the deals are settled. In contrast, at Richerenches in Provence, on Saturday mornings the buyers park their cars and vans with the back facing the street, and display the scales they'll use for weighing in the open trunk. Around 10am, the truffle sellers will start to arrive, carrying cloth bags full of their produce. The buyers open the bags, inspect the contents, and decide on a price. This system clearly depends on a great level of trust between seller and buyer. It would be very easy to slip a few *brumale* and Chinese truffles into a bag, and get away with it – once.

The most important buyers are the courtiers, the people who buy on behalf of the big truffle wholesalers and bottlers, as they represent the wholesalers across all the main markets, and set the prices. There are probably no more than about 20 of them, and they often have very close links with the companies they service. One family in Provence has worked with the Cahors-based Pébeyre truffle business for three generations. They will also buy direct from certain growers, cutting out the middle man, and a grower's relationship with his courtier can be a crucial part of his overall business. After purchase, the courtier will sort the day's truffles, cleaning off the worst of the dirt, and prepare them for the wholesaler. During the season, both courtier and wholesaler will travel a great deal. They may have fleeting meetings in motorway service stations to exchange truffles, almost like drug dealers. Sometimes they run in to problems, as one courtier did at the beginning of 2005 when thieves side-swiped his car, waved guns in his face, and stole the 40kg of black truffle he was carrying. The Pébeyre organisation

Pierre-Jean Pébeyre with his father Jacques during my visit in October 2000.

buys truffle from all over France, Spain and Italy, and Pierre-Jean Pébeyre, the fourth generation of Pébeyres in the truffle business, will spend most of the winter in his car driving around France and Spain.

Once safely back in the wholesaler's premises, the truffles are sorted into grades, and a check will be made to make sure they are what they're meant to be. A key step is taking a small slice off one side of the truffle to see the flesh inside. This process is called caniflage, and allows the trader to judge the maturity of the truffle as well as to check for any stray *brumale* or *uncinatum*. (Black truffles are actually brownish at the beginning of the season when not fully ripe, and become purplish black when at their best.) They are then washed in a special brushing machine to remove any lingering traces of dirt, before being packaged ready for the buyers. Finally they are off by air freight to the restaurants and hotels of the world, ideally arriving while still at their best.

As they travel, the value of the truffles increases dramatically. The price paid by the restaurants is not only higher because the wholesaler has to make a living. There's also the cost of the soil cleaned off the truffles, which is some of the most expensive on the planet. Then there's the grading process, with the lesser grades being much less valuable. And if there are any interlopers to throw out, they'll push the price up as well. The European wholesaler may sell to a secondary wholesaler in another country, or an American wholesaler might buy directly from a larger producer in Europe. Either way, the truffles will be passing through a longish chain, with each step taking a cut. Truffles are also sometimes subject to import duties. Trade within Europe is duty free, but at the time of writing the US was imposing a 100% tariff. By the time a French truffle reaches the US it will inevitably be very expensive, especially after the retailer adds their margin. What might have fetched a few hundred euros per kilo in a French market may be more than a thousand dollars per kilo in an American store. With Italian white truffles, the starting prices are higher, but with no tariff, the increase in price isn't so marked.

The internet is beginning to have an impact on truffle sales, with several French and Italian village markets setting up websites that offer direct sales during the season. One of the first was the market of St Alvère (http://www.truffe-perigord-noir.com/), a charming little village south of Perigueux in the Dordogne. From the grower's point of view, the attractions of internet marketing are obvious. The web opens up a global market, and selling directly to the end user means both growers and consumers should get a better price.

Buyers, however, have to have a huge amount of trust in the quality controls of the market. St Alvère goes to some lengths to reassure web surfers about their quality control, insisting for instance that truffles be washed and graded before they're offered for sale, but you can't sniff truffles to assess their maturity over the internet – yet.

One of the sterilising machines at Marini Truffles in Acqualagna, Italy.

Preserving truffles is still an important business, and little glass jars of cooked truffles are still the only way to buy a truffle during the off-season, at least until New Zealand and Australia have exportable quantities of the fresh kind. The process was invented by a Frenchman called Nicolas Appert in the 1790s, who discovered that food sterilised by heating in a sealed container would keep for long periods without spoiling. In the very early days of preserving truffles, they were sold in little conical glass flasks that have become very collectable, especially in France. The first stage, called the première ebullition ('first boiling'), is done in bulk in most of the large truffle houses. The truffles lose about 20 percent of their weight, and a quantity of flavoursome truffle juice is produced. They also lose a lot of their aroma and flavour. Later in the year, the big cans of truffle are opened up and repackaged in the final containers. They are then cooked and sealed a second time to re-sterilise them before sale. This reduces the aroma and flavour even more. Some producers market their truffles from the first stage of the process, and these are the most likely to resemble the real thing.

Preserved truffles are more expensive than fresh, if only because they lose a lot of their weight in processing. But, by being packaged in fancy jars and sold round the world, there's plenty of room for mark-up and margin to be added. When you finally buy one, it will seem a large price to pay for a little product – and might turn out to be a disappointment.

CHAPTER FIFTEEN
Desert Truffles

THE ROOT OF ALL TRUFFLE CULTURE lies in the sands of the Middle East and North Africa. Here, close relatives of European hypogeous fungi live in association with rock roses and other dry-land plants, and when the conditions are right (normally after early winter rain), they can produce large quantities of truffles. Not so aromatic and tasty as Tuber melanosporum or magnatum, but still good to eat. Desert-dwellers love them. They may even have been the Biblical 'manna from heaven' that is said to have fed the Israelites fleeing from Egypt.

There are more than 30 kinds of desert truffles, all members of the genera *Terfezia* and *Tirmania*. They grow in the hot, dry, scrubby regions around the Mediterranean, from southern Spain, through north Africa from Morocco to Egypt, to the Middle East and Turkey. Other species grow in Sardinia, in southern Africa, and there are similar fungi in Australia that were much appreciated by the aboriginal people. Many kinds are eaten avidly throughout the Arab world, but the commonest are a pale whitish brown, roughly spherical but often knobbly with lobes and bumps. They grow to

tennis-ball size or slightly larger, and are slightly spongy, without a very pronounced aroma or flavour. Another type, more highly valued, is reddish and dark, with a denser flesh and stronger flavour.

As we saw when looking at the history of truffle use, the early civilisations of Mesopotamia, between the Tigris and Euphrates in

A good haul of deser truffles being offere by this street seller in Marsa Matruh, Egypt. (John Feeney/Saua Aramco World/PADIA)

Unearthing a desert truffle. *(John Feeney/Saudi Aramco World/PADIA)*

what is today Iraq, and in the Nile valley of Egypt, would have been very familiar with desert truffles. That knowledge and appreciation was inherited by the Greek and Roman cultures that followed them. Most of the references to truffles in classical works are almost certainly to desert truffles, and the Latin name for truffle, terfez, is clearly derived from terfas, the name given to them by the nomadic inhabitants of the western Sahara and Morocco. The myths and sayings associated with these fungi then became associated with European truffles. There are plenty of references in literature to the ancient belief that truffles were formed when lightning hit the ground. This is still a part of the received wisdom of desert truffle hunters in Syria. The Bedouin nickname for truffles translates as "potatoes of thunder". This echoes the French belief that

Typical desert truffle country in Egypt. The small shrubs include rock roses, plant hosts for the truffles. *(John Feeney/Saudi Aramco World/PADIA)*

The flesh of desert truffles is very diffe ent to that of "true" truffles - less dense, without marked vei ing - reminiscent of puffballs. (*John Feeney/ Saudi Aramco World/PADIA*

late summer thunderstorms are crucial for getting a good crop of Périgord blacks, but the real link is the need for rainfall to trigger and sustain fruiting. In the desert, as in France, with too little rain the crop will be poor. Desert truffles are, however, much better adapted to dry conditions, and too much water is probably as bad for them as too little. One other reputation of truffles also may have its roots in the desert: they're believed to be aphrodisiacs there, as well.

There is a very active truffle trade in the Arab world. They can be found in winter in markets throughout the region, and in a good season are often available in large quantities at prices well below those of European truffles. In Iraq, they are a seasonal luxury, called kamaa or chima; in Saudi Arabia they're called faqa' or kama, and in Syria, kamah. After early winter rains (and thunderstorms) the collectors will be out in force. In Egypt they often have to contend with old Second World War minefields, but in Iraq and Kuwait there are more modern battlefield risks to be faced. Collectors will be looking for the right plants, scrubby members of the genus *Helioanthemum*, and around them the little cracks and humps that show truffles are growing underneath. Early morning or evening light can help to show the little humps in the sand, but the truffles often break surface and get eaten by small animals and birds – even camels. In a dry season, the canny hunter will look for small hollows which may have retained more moisture for the fungi.

Once harvested, the truffles have to be shipped to market quickly. They have a short shelf life, around five days, and don't take kindly to being stored in plastic or under refrigeration. An Egyptian truffle might be air-freighted to the Gulf or Saudi Arabia and be on a dinner table within a day of being dug up. Because they are relatively plentiful, desert truffles are used as the centrepiece of dishes, not as a flavouring, and are often cooked in robust sauces and stews. Round truffles are more sought-after than larger, knobbly ones, because smoother truffles are less likely to have sand and grit lodged inside them. In any event, the truffles are carefully peeled and washed before cooking, and are usually cut up into cubes, presumably to make sure no sand finds its way into the finished dish. They can also be served raw, in salads.

Experiments with the cultivation of various species of *Terfezia* are well advanced in Israel and Spain, and it may not be long before desert truffle truffières are having an impact on the marketplace.

In southern Africa, *Terfezia pfeilii*, the Namibian or Kalahari truffle, known to the Saan as !Naba (! is a sort of click made by the tongue touching the roof of the mouth) and other tribes as omatumbula, can be found in May and June after rain. They are pear-shaped and dark brown, and ripe specimens are said to have a flavour as good as any European truffle. Like their cousins further north, they're usually found by a tell-tale pattern of cracks on the soil surface, although baboons and bat-eared foxes also love them and can lead collectors to good sites.

In a good year, desert truffles can be found in great quantities. (John Feeney/Saudi Aramco World/ PADIA)

CHAPTER SIXTEEN

Buying Truffles

IN THIS CHAPTER I WILL NOT ENAMOUR MYSELF to the producers of preserved truffles, truffle oil, truffle powder or truffle-flavoured flour, because I am going to argue that the only way to really appreciate any kind of truffle is to eat a carefully prepared dish using the freshest, ripest truffles. That other stuff might give you some kind of truffle experience, but it will not be the fullest expression of what these fungi can do for food. Real truffle may never have been involved in their manufacture. Mine is the counsel of perfection, because if you don't understand the true potential of truffles, you will always misunderstand or underestimate them.

Unfortunately, buying good, ripe, fresh truffles is not a trivial undertaking. Even in France and Italy, where fresh truffle can be found in marketplaces and shops throughout the season, there is uncertainty and risk. For a foreigner, it takes time to learn how the various truffle markets work, and a certain willingness to experiment with large sums of money. In the US, the local truffles are available at much lower prices, but identifying the best, ripest ones

Tuber magnatum and Tuber aestivum on sale at the truffle market in Alba. The individual truffles are priced for display.

may take more fondling and sniffing than most shopkeepers will
tolerate. There is also the possibility of being ripped off: of being
sold a Chinese truffle that's posing as a Périgord black, or a bianchetto pretending to be an Italian white.

So here are the principles I reckon you should you follow. First,
and most important, truffles are seasonal food. They should be
eaten in their season – that is, when they are at their ripest and
best – and not before or after. In France, although it is traditional
to have black truffle over Christmas, the experts say they are not
at their best until the middle of January. In the US, you should not
buy Oregon white truffles before December or you risk disappointment. There is an obvious exception, however. If you can get hold
of a New Zealand or Australian-grown Périgord black truffle, it will
be at its best in July, exactly six months out of season with respect
to the northern hemisphere.

Each truffle has its own season. The summer truffle is probably
at its best in late summer and autumn. The Burgundy truffle is a
late autumn and early winter truffle, and overlaps with the Périgord
black, which is in season from mid-December to March, but at its
best (in France) in January. The Italian white truffle is an autumn
truffle, in season from October to December. The bianchetto is a
mid-winter to early spring truffle.

There are exceptions to these rules, of course. Périgord blacks
grown in warmer areas may be available earlier than those from
cooler districts, but may also lack the depth of flavour and finesse
of the cool-climate product. It is possible to obtain fresh truffle
all year round, as they claim in Acqualagna in Italy, but you will be
pushing to get really good stuff in the northern hemisphere spring.

If you are working with the seasons, you should also match your
expectation to the truffle. The summer truffle, *Tuber aestivum*, is
a very worthwhile fungus, tasty and good to eat, but it is cheaper
and not in the same league as a Périgord black. Do not expect it to
transform a meal in the same way. Choose a dish that will be complemented by the truffle, rather than one that depends on it. The
Italian white, for example, is normally served with rather bland
risotto or pasta accompaniments, the better to shine, but a less aromatic truffle served with the same backing dishes will struggle to
impress anyone.

Price is obviously an issue. Recipes that call for "several ripe truffles" are not very helpful, and those that specify an exact amount
may simply give you wallet shock when you hit the shops. The only
guidance I can give is to buy as much as you can afford, and then
don't try and stretch the truffle too far. If you want to impress

guests with truffle at a dinner party, then it's best to aim for one outstanding dish that everyone will remember. In the restaurant trade, the same is true but the economics are different. The temptation to stretch a little truffle a long way may be difficult to resist, but push it too far and a dish that should be the highlight of your menu could turn out to be an expensive disappointment for the customer. Better to make your truffle dish a blackboard item, limiting the number of servings per night according to the amount of truffle on hand, than to put it into a standard menu and be tempted to get by with second-class truffle – or worse, to cover up shortages with truffle oil.

In one respect, restaurants have an advantage over the independent gourmet: they buy truffle regularly and in bigger quantities, and can afford to deal with a supplier who will meet their quality criteria. With large sums of money changing hands, trust becomes an important part of the deal. The onus is on the supplier to get things right. Deliver a bad batch, and you lose a client. An individual, buying only small quantities and only infrequently, lacks that clout. Much depends on where you live. If you can get to a European market, try to get local advice about where to go and how to buy. Perhaps you can buy direct from a grower; many trufficulteurs will sell directly to the public because they get a better price that way. In New Zealand, buying from a grower is the only way to get fresh truffle. There are, as yet, no local wholesalers or distributors. Most of the world's top cities will have at least a few retailers who stock truffle in season, but be sure that they let you check each truffle for quality. Sniffing is essential, even in Fortnum & Mason (perhaps especially so, given the price).

In Chapter 17 I provide a few recipes that are at the core of truffle cuisine – but first, a few words about some of the other truffle products out there. As we saw earlier, most truffle oils are entirely artificial. The availability of scientifically concocted truffle flavourings has led to a dramatic increase in the number of products on retailers' shelves with "truffle" on the label. Some are good; others are not. Experiment by all means, but read the small print. Look at what you're getting. This is especially true of preserved or bottled truffles. The best of these can be good, but inevitably have less intense flavours than the fresh product. If you have first-quality preserved *Tuber melanosporum* from a good supplier, you will have something worth eating, but check the label on the bottle carefully. Many little bottles will shyly admit, in the tiniest lettering, that they contain *Tuber aestivum* or even *Tuber indicum*. In that case, an already mild truffle will probably have been rendered tasteless by the bottling process, and you will certainly be wasting your money.

Frozen truffles are not worth the bother. Frost-damaged fresh truffles are not considered saleable in France, so keeping them in your freezer is definitely not advised. I keep some frozen truffle for dog training. It has a characteristic, musky sort of smell, recognisably truffle but not necessarily something you'd want to eat. I may have to make an exception for truffles that are cryogenically frozen, i.e. frozen at a very low temperature, usually by plunging them into liquid nitrogen. Some authorities maintain that this preserves delicate flavours, provided that the truffles are stored below -18°C and used shaved from the frozen state. I cannot comment on this, having never encountered such truffle, but if you do, and they taste good, let me know. Dried or powdered truffle is also sometimes available. I find it hard to believe that top-quality fresh truffle is being deliberately dried (which evaporates the vast majority of the flavour) and powdered, so if it has a strong truffle aroma I would suspect that this comes from the same source as that in truffle oil. Use at your own risk.

Finally, a quality-control tip. If you suspect you have some Chinese or other lesser infiltrators in a batch of Périgord truffles, this is how to sort them out without having to learn a great deal of mycology. Take the truffles and put each one in a separate, sealed container. Place the containers in a warm place for an hour. Much like warming brandy to release its flavours, this gets the truffle aromas moving. Genuine Périgord black truffles will release a whirlwind of aroma which will leave you in no doubt as to their origin. Chinese truffles will release some scent, and it will be a little like the Périgord, but only a pale shadow of the real thing, lacking intensity, complexity and finesse.

A range of truffle products from Tartufi Marini in Acqualagna, Italy.

CHAPTER SEVENTEEN

The Defining Dishes

THIS IS NOT A RECIPE BOOK, but it would be ridiculous to write so much about the glorious complexity of the world of truffles without giving you some idea of how to use them properly. If you need lots of truffle recipes, sophisticated ways to employ their strengths and impress your guests or customers, there are several suggestions in the Sources section at the end of this book.

For the defining dishes presented here, I've stuck with tradition. The recipes below are stalwarts of truffle cuisine for one very good reason: they work. They make the most of the truffle they use. They may be simple, but in this case less is definitely more.

Once again, I am going to offer the counsel of perfection. Use only the finest fresh truffle you can lay your hands on, and buy as much as you can afford. Match the truffle with finest-quality ingredients. If the recipe specifies egg, let it be a free-range egg from happy chickens which lay to an accompaniment of classical music. If rice is required, don't dig out some stale old grains from the back of the cupboard, but find some really good carnaroli or arborio in a lovingly hand-sewn sack that has the maker's life story on the back of the label. Don't cut corners. If you have to leave the truffle to work its magic for a day or two, then leave it. There's a good reason for taking the time. And don't make these dishes when you are stressed out, unless making them is your particular form of therapy. Eating truffle should be a special experience. Make it so.

Preparing truffles is pretty straightforward. They need to be washed and brushed to remove any soil that may be clinging to the skin. Just brush them gently under running water, then dry carefully. A toothbrush is good; use anything too hard and you risk bruising or marking the more delicate truffles. Line a glass jar or plastic container that has a tight seal with kitchen paper or tissues (not the aloe vera impregnated kind, please), and put the dried truffles inside. Close the lid carefully. You want the truffle smell to stay inside, not to escape and flavour everything in your fridge. Truffled milk is not something I'd recommend. Put the container in the warmest part of the fridge. If storing for any length of time, check at least daily, and wipe away any moisture that collects – though I strongly recommend using the truffle as soon as possible. It will already have been several days out of the ground, and will only have at best a week or so of shelf-life left. Truffles give off moisture steadily, and will eventually either rot or dry up. In either case you will have wasted a lot of money.

White truffles can generally be used without any further preparation, but the Périgord black may require peeling. The skin can be quite tough, though it varies a lot. If you do peel, peel thinly, and reserve the peelings – there's plenty of flavour in them.

As far as truffle tools are concerned, there is only one real essential: a truffle cutter, shaver or slicer. These have a very sharp, adjustable blade and are available in good kitchen stores, sometimes labelled as chocolate shavers. You simply rub the truffle along the face of the shaver against the blade, and lovely thin slices of truffle drop from the other side. You can't do this even with a very sharp knife. If you've ever had white truffle in an Italian restaurant, you may have seen one wielded by the head waiter. Like all trendy kitchen gear, you can either buy the stainless-steel version for a modest price, or pay a small fortune for something a little more fashionable. I have a stainless-steel one, and it's fine.

Simple stainless-steel truffle shaver: the one essential kitchen tool for truffle enthusiasts.

Brouillade (truffled scrambled eggs)

All truffles have an affinity with the humble egg. When Provençal rabassiers or caveurs bring their truffles home from the hunt, their preferred dish is this apparently simple scrambled egg. In Italy too, the white truffle is magnificent in an omelette. This recipe is for the Périgord black truffle, but can be adapted to white truffle very easily.

at least 50g/2oz Périgord black truffle
6 free-range eggs
butter or goose fat

The Provençal standard preparation time for this dish is three days. You might get away with only two days, but remember what I said about cutting corners. Steel yourself to be patient.

Find a glass jar or plastic container large enough to hold the eggs and truffle and line it with a paper towel or tissue. Put the eggs and truffle inside, seal the jar tightly, and put it in the warmest part of the fridge. Eggs are porous, so the powerful perfume of the truffle will find its way through the shells and infuse the white and yolk with its wonderful scent.

The eggs will make a perfectly respectable truffle omelette or scrambled eggs after two days, even if you put no truffle into the pan (the truffle can be used in another dish) – but that is not the real brouillade, just a pale shadow. For the real thing, we must use all the truffle.

Peel the truffle carefully, and slice the peelings into thin strips. Heat your chosen fat (goose fat would be the Périgord choice) over a low heat, and toss in the truffle strips. Beat and season the eggs. Slice two-thirds of the truffle and add the shavings to the eggs. Stir briefly and put in the pan. As the eggs start to catch, pull towards the centre of the pan – this is the classic scrambled-egg technique. It should be lightly cooked, still fairly liquid; golden and glistening, studded with black. Decorate with the remaining truffle, sliced thinly. Serve immediately in a warm bowl, with thick slices of the best bread you can bake or buy and a good, robust red wine. Something from Tricastin, perhaps.

You can do exactly the same thing with *Tuber magnatum*, but you can avoid the three-day waiting time (though a day or two with the eggs is still a good idea). Just shave half your truffle into the beaten eggs and stir them in. Leave them to stand for a few minutes, and then make an omelette rather than a brouillade. An Italian omelette (frittata) should be firmer than scrambled eggs, but it should still have a melting, golden middle. Shave the remaining truffle over the omelette as it leaves the pan. More red wine required: a good Chianti, perhaps.

And while you've got those truffled eggs in the fridge, can I suggest a millionaire's breakfast? Fry two of the aromatic eggs in a little extra-virgin olive oil, and serve with some shavings of truffle on top. Black or white, it doesn't matter. Good days start with truffled eggs.

Périgord black truffles work really well with foie gras, the fat liver of overfed ducks and geese, another of the traditional products of that part of France. Silky smooth, amazingly rich; an ethereal essence of goose or duck. Marry it with truffle and you have a wonderful combination of flavour and aroma. When buying a pot of foie gras with truffles, or a paté de foie gras truffée, support the artisanal producers of France, who will use good foie gras and the proper truffle. Too many of the mass-produced versions will use inferior livers, and may substitute something cheaper for the truffle. Little rubbery chunks of tasteless black stuff (perhaps chopped up trompettes de mort mushrooms, Chinese truffle or brumale) do not a great paté make.

Foie gras leads us nicely into the next truffle classic, tournedos Rossini. The French composer Rossini was a noted gourmet who kept tables at many of Paris's top restaurants, including the Maison Dorée, whose chef Casimir Moisson created the famed tournedos. A Rossini sauce, by the way, consists of a good demi-glace (stock) mixed with foie gras and truffles – and that's what goes into tournedos Rossini. The truffles are first peeled and gently poached in Madeira (they can then be stored in a cool place for later use – a classic chef's technique with truffle, it preserves them very effectively). Meanwhile you cook a slice of fillet steak, a slice of fresh foie gras, and fry a croute of bread. Put the steak on the croute, top it with a few slices of truffle and the foie gras, and then surround with a sauce made with the truffled Madeira and some good strong beef stock, whisked together with a little butter.

Black truffles also work wonders with chickens. Here is how to make the classic *poularde en demi-deuil*, or 'chicken in half mourning'– basically, poached truffled chicken. Buy a good chicken – *poulet de Bresse*, if you can, but a corn-fed, free-range chicken at the very least. Push slices of truffle between the skin and the flesh on the breast and the outside of the legs. If you're careful, you can lift the skin off the breast with your fingers, but on the legs you'll have to make small incisions with a knife. Make a neat arrangement of the truffle slices, covering as much of the flesh as you can afford. Cover the bird and put it in the fridge for a few hours. The truffle flavours will work their way into the flesh, and the longer you leave it the better. Finally, simply cook the chicken in a big pot of vegetable stock for around two hours. Serve the truffled chicken stock as a soup course, then cut the chicken into quarters and serve with a little rice and some of the vegetables that you've cooked alongside the chicken in the stock. If you want to tart this classic up a little, you might stuff the chicken with a stuffing made of the minced heart, liver and giblets,

Truffled roast chicken: the slices of black truffle show through the crispy skin.

with some good sausage meat, seasonings and truffle pieces.

A chicken truffled in the above manner can also be roasted. Heat your oven to its highest temperature. Rub the chicken with butter, season it liberally with salt and freshly ground black pepper, and put a glass of white wine in the roasting pan. Let the chicken roast for an hour (or less – it depends on how hot your oven is), basting it occasionally until the skin is crisp and a deep chestnut brown. Check that it's cooked through by sticking a knife into the thickest part of the leg and breast and making sure that the juices are running clear, then let it rest in the oven with the door open for 15 minutes. Serve with the pan juices, perhaps refreshed with a little more wine.

Contrary to reports in the Western medi *the Chinese enjoy their truffles too: a Szechuan-style chic en and truffle dish.*
(*Yu Fuqiang*)

If you're after even greater refinement, or want to save some time, you can do the same sort of thing with chicken breasts. Buy some good chicken breasts (or supremes: the ones that have a bit of bone left at one end) and make cuts in them about two-thirds of the way through, about a centimetre apart. Into each cut, slip a chunk of truffle. Cover the breasts and leave them to absorb the truffle flavour for as long as possible. Put the breasts in an oven dish with a little oil and a splash of wine, then roast them in a hot oven for 20 minutes. For a slightly fancier presentation, wrap the breasts in prosciutto before leaving them to truffle themselves.

Tuber magnatum, the most expensive truffle in the world, doesn't stand up to cooking in the same way as the Périgord black. It is usually served simply shaved over a risotto or pasta dish – but 'simple' doesn't mean unsophisticated. A risotto to act as a foil for the Italian white truffle is a simple affair, with the truffle providing all the class you could want.

Truffle risotto

> *1.5 L chicken stock*
> *1 onion, finely chopped*
> *125 g butter*
> *400 g high-quality risotto rice*
> *1 glass white wine*
> *75 g best parmesan cheese, freshly grated*
> *as much* Tuber magnatum *as you can afford*

Use the best risotto rice you can find – arborio or carnaroli – and some very good chicken stock (home-made is always best). Heat

Desert truffles also have an affinity for egg dishes. (John Feeney/Saudi Aramco World/ PADIA)

the stock and keep it simmering on the stove next to the pan in which you're cooking the risotto. Start by sweating the onion in a little butter, and when it is clear, add the rice and stir until well coated. Throw in the wine, and stir until it has all been absorbed. Then add the stock, a ladleful at a time, allowing the rice to absorb it before adding more. Stir more or less continuously. After 20 minutes the rice should be nicely cooked: soft but retaining a firm centre – *al dente*, in other words – and the whole thing should be creamy and thick, not too soupy. Take the pan off the heat and stir in the rest of the butter and the Parmesan (do I need to remind you to use only the best parmigiano reggiano?) Shave half of the truffle into the rice, and then serve with more slices of truffle on top.

The same principles apply when you're making pasta as a base for white truffles. Make your own pasta dough (using good flour, the best eggs, and so on), roll it out and cut it into tagliatelle (wide noodle strips). I won't give a recipe: you'll find guidance in the works of Antonio Carluccio and Marcella Hazan. As a last resort, and if time is

Tasmanian truffle grower's break-fast. (Tim Terry)

short, buy good dried Italian pasta. Cook the pasta in a large pan of well-salted water. When it's done, drain it, dress it with butter and parmesan and half of your truffle. Shave the remainder of the truffle on top of the pasta as you serve it.

Another Italian staple can work well with truffle: pizza. There are two approaches to a truffle pizza. You can either shave fresh truffle on to the hot cheese as it leaves the oven, and then leave the pizza for a few seconds to allow the flavour to develop, or you can shave the truffle onto the pizza base, and then cover it with the finest mozzarella you can lay your hands on. This is a truffled pizza bianca, and is superb when cooked in the searing heat of a wood-fired oven.

All three of the above dishes will work perfectly with good Oregon white truffles or a ripe bianchetto, but are at their best with *magnatum*. I will admit that it can be a little off-putting in a restaurant to pay a supplement for a truffle risotto and then find that you only get a few shavings on the top. But if the truffle is good, it will be an experience to remember.

American readers can substitute Oregon white and black truffles for the classic European species and not feel short-changed. In fact, if you can find good ripe Oregon truffles, you probably have a better chance of a really good truffle experience than trying to use imported truffle that may well be near the end of its shelf life. However, I can't resist offering you one amazing recipe from Jack Czarnecki at The Joel Palmer House Restaurant in Dayton, Oregon. He has married the fruity, chocolatey flavours of the Oregon black truffle with coffee, to create the world's first truffle latte. Here's his recipe:

"To one third cup hot simple syrup [two cups of sugar dissolved in one cup of water] add one ounce of finely chopped ripe Oregon black truffle. The syrup must be hot so that the heat extracts the flavour. Let it cool to room temperature, and refrigerate. This is the flavour extract, which can then be added to the latte just as a vanilla extract would be added. A tablespoon should be plenty. Add whipped cream on top and add a shaving or two of fresh black truffle, and there you have it." And I can't wait to try it!

CHAPTER EIGHTEEN
Fungal Feasting

Acqualagna, autumn 2000.

DOTTORE GIANLUIGI GREGORI, head of truffle research for the Marche, was negotiating his way back to our table when an explosion of very Italian greeting erupted from a corner of the little Acqualagna restaurant. Gigi, as he is known to his friends (and there are many of them), circled the table, grinning, and before long I was summoned over to join him. We were to eat lunch with a friend of his, the owner and chef of a restaurant on the coast that specialises in seafood and "food of the forest". Sergio Lani, a large man who is as generous as his waistline, had been out truffle hunting that morning with friends, and a very fine specimen of *Tuber magnatum* sat on the table in front of him. Several hundred thousand lire worth, at least. This we were compelled to eat, while Gigi occasionally translated parts of the conversation for my benefit. After an hour I had absolutely no idea what was going on, but I'd eaten a lot of wonderful white truffle.

The following evening, as I was preparing to thank Gigi for acting as my guide to Italy's leading truffle-producing region, and looking forward to a quiet hour or two writing up notes in my hotel, he announced that we would be off to Sergio's restaurant for dinner. "He invited us yesterday," he said.

Lunch in Acqualagna. Sergio grates generous quantities of freshly dug magnatum *on to a plate of pasta.*

"You remember?" Since the good Dottore speaks no English, and I no Italian, we were conversing in, on my part, very rusty French. Scope for plenty of misunderstandings.

I wasn't too keen, I must confess. Misano Adriatico is 80 km from Gigi's office in the Marche hills, it was dark and raining hard, and he wanted me to take my car "because it will be quicker". Given that he toured the district in a battered old 4WD, this was certainly true, but I uncharitably suspected that I was being set up so that Gigi could have a good night out with his mates.

I can tell you nothing about the drive there: I followed Gigi's directions and tried to avoid hitting anything. The restaurant itself, Il Coccio, is pleasant, large, and well lit, with linen tablecloths, a lot of polished wood and a pizza oven. We were ushered straight into the kitchen. In boxes against the far wall, fresh porcini (*Boletus edulis*) were arrayed ready for slicing. In a pan on the stove, a mixture of mushrooms sizzled gently for crostini. Sergio opened a large Tupperware box, apparently stuffed with tissue paper. There was much grinning, loud talking, and earnest shaking of my hand. The good Dottore sniffed his way through a selection of white truffles as they emerged from the tissue, commenting on the aroma, the perfume, the power of each one. He was selecting the one he wanted to eat later.

Now the perfume of *Tuber magnatum* is something to savour and treasure, both delicate and powerful; but in Sergio's kitchen, the smell was like a sledgehammer. As he opened the milky plastic box, my nostrils were almost slammed back into my head and my stomach began turning cartwheels in expectation. We retired to the bar for a prosecco. Another of Gigi's friends arrived, a mushroom fanatic who happens to be fairly senior in the forestry business in the region. He had been lured out on a foul night by the promise of a mushroom feast. I began to get quietly excited, and the prosecco had nothing to do with it.

The first course was ovoli, thinly sliced with parmesan, some salt and pepper, and good olive oil. Ovoli are *Amanita caesaria* (known as oranges in France), reckoned to be the finest of all mushrooms, even if they are closely related to the death cap. They are a bright orange in colour, with white flesh and pale gills, They are rare and expensive, and I had never tasted them before. I sat up, a broad grin on my face, and tucked in. The taste was similar to ordinary button mushrooms, but more refined — somehow more aristocratic. They were a delight. This course was accompanied by crispy pizza bread, hot from the oven, but before I could reach for another spoonful, a porcini salad arrived. Again, thinly sliced mushrooms,

Dottore Gianluigi "Gigi" Gregori shows off his truffle trees before dragging me off to dinner.

with parmesan and olive oil, but this time with the interesting addition of very thin shavings of celery. Brilliant; a more powerful, up-front flavour than the ovoli, a sort of essence of mushroom. And before we could even begin to sample that, a plate of crostini with ovoli and porcini fried together. This was all accompanied by a very nice Rosso Picino Superiore, much conversation in Italian and a little in broken French. We were having interesting discussions about terroir, genetics, and how the finest porcini are found not in the places of greatest abundance, but where they have to struggle to grow. At least that's what I thought we were talking about.

The second course arrived only after we had cleared the three large platters of mushrooms. A white truffle frittata, quite firm in texture, with some white truffle shaved into the mixture and much more shaved on top. I am not exaggerating when I say that it announced its arrival the moment it left the kitchen. The power of the scent of white truffle is quite amazing. It was a large omelette, and filling.

Next up was the pasta: tagliatelle with a porcini and cream sauce. Quite delicious, but by this time we were all beginning to feel a little full, not to say stuffed. We attempted to get the waiter to restrain Sergio in the kitchen, to stem the flow of marvellous food, but we failed. One more dish was already in the oven, and we would have to do it justice. A dish of grilled porcini caps arrived — the large flat caps slashed in the thickest part, dressed with a little oil and salt, and then grilled until beginning to char. Outside they were beginning to crisp up; inside they were meltingly delicious.

The fresh mushroom tastes very different to the dried: milder, less musty, less pervasive, but Sergio's grilled caps combined the two in a completely beguiling way. As simple dishes go, it was a triumph, and we cleared that plate very quickly indeed.

We finished with a little sorbetto, then an espresso, and before we were allowed to leave, Sergio dived into his cellar, and emerged clutching a bottle of grappa di pinot nero – one of the most prized of grappas, and not, as I had assumed, made from pinot noir grapes but derived from the black pine. Over my protestations, I was required to drink a generous tot to fortify myself against the drive. Nobody seemed to pay any money, so I can't comment on price, but I knew as I stepped out into the rain that I had just eaten a meal that would end up being mythologised in memory. Friends and family will grow tired of the references to Sergio's porcini, and my ascent to boring old duffer will move up another notch. But it was, and will be, worth it.

Ristorante Il Coccio, *Piazza Gramsci 51/A, 47843 Misano Adriatico, Italy. Tel: +39 0541 615593*

CHAPTER NINETEEN
The Truffle Tour

THE PLANE WAS SMALL and the seats smaller. It was packed to the gills. The French passengers returning home looked, as French travellers usually do, automatically stylish. There were no berets or baguettes, just duty-free and coats slung over carry-on bags that were too big to fit under the seat in front. The tickets were cheap, London to Bordeaux for something like £50, and I was in a good mood. My smile owed nothing to the dire lunch I'd grabbed in the terminal at Gatwick, and everything to the fact that, while getting some French and Italian cash on my credit card (pre-Euro, this), the cashier, a rather charming young lady, had asked my date of birth. "1954," I'd offered, and she'd looked up and said, "Don't you mean '64?"

This was late October 2000, and by the time the flight decanted in Bordeaux it was dark and raining. I had a reservation at L'Auberge de la Truffe in Sorges, a village about 140 kilometres east, beyond Perigueux. I would be too late for dinner, but in my dreadful French I had requested a petit plat for when I arrived. The

The Auberge de la Truffe in Sorges: specialists in truffle cuisine, and petits plats that are far from petit.

journey was terrible. Not only was I still slightly jet-lagged and driving a strange car on the wrong side of the road for the first time for four years, but I had no navigator, it was still raining, and French trucks take no prisoners.

The truffle museum at Sorges: note the large truffle hanging off the wall.

The hotel in Sorges was small and welcoming. The plat – two large slices of very fine, very rare fillet steak, two slices of a mousseline of some local fish, a pichet of rouge, two big hunks of cheese and a large slice of a French bread-puddingy tart with almonds – was far from petit, and restored my faith in France and humanity in general.

My trip had been some time in the planning. The general idea was to visit the main truffle-growing and harvesting areas of France and Italy, seeing key places and meeting local growers, talking, listening and taking photographs for this book. If you ignore Spain, a journey from Bordeaux to Bologna via Provence, with some diversions and a finishing flourish in the Marche province of Italy, will take you through Europe's premier truffle regions. It is also a trip through some of the most beautiful parts of that continent, taking in superb wine appellations, scenic grandeur, history on many levels, and most importantly, the gourmet cultures that have so influenced the world's tastes.

This truffle "grand tour" is best done independently, by car. Very few of the highlights are on main roads or near big cities, and the freedom of having your own transport means that you can adapt your schedule to the weather and your mood. The conservative might pre-book rooms at strategically located hotels and inns from the Logis de France or Michelin guides, but if you're travelling out of the main tourist seasons and away from their well-trodden routes, you can quite easily book as you go. There is always the chance you'll stumble across a superb little hotel that serves divine food, and a risk (albeit slight) that you'll end up somewhere gloomy with bad food. But bad food in France is seldom inedible, only disappointing. Driving in France means driving on the wrong side of the road if you're from Britain, Japan, Australia or New Zealand, but the rest of the world will feel right at home. Off the motorways, in the countryside, the driving is often wonderful. Michelin maps indicate particularly scenic routes with green lines. They are worth following.

I started in Sorges because, apart from being a rather charming old village, it houses the Écomusée de la Truffe, a reputedly fine museum of truffle history and culture. I say reputedly, because when I got there on a misty Monday morning it was closed, and so my experience of it is strictly virtual. Still, if you wish to embark on a truffle tour of Europe, I would start at Sorges. Just check the museum opening times. From there I drove south, heading for St Alvère, the first French village to put its truffle market on the internet. Near the village is the Truffière de la Bergerie, where Hugues Martin and his wife have a charming gite (holiday cottage) for hire. They offer guided tours of their 12 hectares of truffière, and in season will show their dogs working. They provided me with a fine lunch and some very nice vin de noix (a concoction of red wine, brandy and walnut leaves), but not too much of it as I had further to drive.

Just south of St Alvère the route crosses the Dordogne. The sensible tourist (as opposed to the obsessed truffle researcher) will divert up the valley to see some of the great sights of the region, the villages clinging to the steep cliffs of the gorge. There are truffles all around, so you needn't feel guilty. I headed deep into the countryside to spend a few days in a gite run by a couple who make foie gras. From there I was able to explore Cahors, visiting the Pébeyre head office, and drive around the oak woodlands and villages of the surrounding limestone plateau. All around there's evidence of the truffle boom of the 19th century, and in Lalbenque, one of the region's most active truffle markets. Worth a few days of anyone's time.

Heading for Provence, I spent a day on the péage (toll motorway) driving from Agen (prune capital of the world) to Avignon, and a little hotel near Carpentras in the Vaucluse. It's a long drive, but the motorway is fast and I was there by mid-afternoon. I stopped

The truffle market building at St Alvère in the Périgord.

The little hilltop town of Barbaresco, above Alba. Vineyards and haze nut orchards cling t the slopes all round.

by a little orchard to drink in the view of Mt Ventoux, and stepped on some wild thyme. As the smell wafted up to my nose, I began to understand why Provence exerts such a strong pull on all sorts of people. If you're on a less strict schedule, I would suggest avoiding the motorways and heading from Cahors through Villefranche and on through Millau to the chestnut-clad mountains of the Cevennes. Fascinating countryside, and at Millau, a superb and vertiginous modern bridge to drive over.

Carpentras is one of the key truffle markets of the region, beaten only by Richerenches to the north in terms of volumes sold. The slopes of Mt Ventoux are covered in truffières, and as you drive towards the Alps lavender farms compete with truffières for space. It would be easy to spend weeks in the area, enjoying the food and wine, but the truffle tourist has to head on to St Saturnin les Apt and pay homage to the statue of the father of truffle-growing, Joseph Talon. It rained when I was there, which is why the photograph of him in this book looks a little gloomy.

The journey out of France towards the Piedmont is easily achieved on the motorway, but there is one diversion you should make: to Chez Bruno at Lorgues, the restaurant of Clément Bruno, a chef who prides himself on offering truffle cuisine throughout the year. I didn't get the chance to eat there, but those who have done wax lyrical about Bruno's meals.

The truffle-lover's tour now moves on to the home of the white truffle, and the route turns north, away from the sea and into the Piedmont. The motorway to Turin offers an easy way through the hills, but to get the full experience you should approach Alba along one of Michelin's green-lined routes. As you wind down valleys or along ridges, finding towns set high above rivers that obviously flood with some regularity, you begin to get a feel for the place. On a clear day, the hills recede into the distance, and across the flat valley floor at the head of the Po, where Torino bustles and smokes, you see the white-capped Alps on the horizon. I didn't. Low cloud was capping all the ridges I was driving along.

In Alba, the truffle market is the obvious attraction, but the whole area is also famous for its wines, and happy hours can be spent wandering from one castellated hilltop winery to another, tasting and admiring. From Alba, the tour heads east along the southern edge of the Po valley, through Asti and Alessandria to Piacenza and Parma. The names of the towns begin to suggest food, and a stop in any will be repaid with artworks, food shops and all the Italian style you could wish for.

And if you choose the autostrada, as I did, then be prepared for Ferraris to burn past as you bypass Modena. The driving is – how shall I put this – a little more *frenzied* than you will find in France. Still, it will be worth it when you get to Bologna, famous in the English-speaking for the meat sauce named after it (that Italians call ragu). Apart from all the history and culture, there are truffles in the hills to the south, every bit as good as those of Alba and just as eagerly sought after.

If you still have time, Florence and Tuscany are only a few hours' drive south, with their own truffle sites to visit. Perhaps the market at San Miniato, halfway between Florence and Pisa? Or hammer on down the autostrada to the Marche, and visit Urbino and Acqualagna, the latter boasting fresh truffle for 12 months of the year.

This itinerary could be done in two weeks (I did it in slightly less) but three weeks would be better, and allow more time for non-truffle diversions. If you want to experience the French truffle world in action, you should probably plan to travel in winter, from mid-December onwards; while if you want to fill up on *magnatum*, you'll need to be in Italy between October and December. To combine both is difficult, but you might try starting in Italy in late November, and then hit Provence in December. Better still, do Italy in October, have a break for Christmas, and then hit France in January, when *melanosporum* is at its best.

CHAPTER TWENTY
Grow Your Own

THROUGHOUT THIS BOOK I've been keen to establish just how professional a truffle grower I am, or intend to be. The return on our investment in infected trees should be good, and my fruitful retirement planning will be the envy of my friends. With luck. But financial prudence is only a cover story. The real truth is that I'm trying to grow truffles because I want to eat them.

If everything goes to plan, Limestone Hills will have ripe truffles for the dinner table from autumn until spring. The season will start with Burgundy truffle, move on to Périgord black truffle in early winter, and finish with the bianchetto in late winter. Add in to the mix meals of porcini and saffron milk caps, and fungal feasts will play a big part in our home cuisine. I won't have to spend a fortune to live like a millionaire.

I could emulate this lifestyle quite easily by living in France or Italy and having lots of money. Not having the latter precludes the former, so I live in New Zealand and grow my own. I happen to think that New Zealand is a great place to do this, but readers in other parts of the planet can also have a go at doing it themselves.

Starting small: Limestone Hills' young truffle trees (in their protective boxes) being watered spring 1997.

Anywhere that truffles can be found in the wild, they can also be grown in captivity. Bianchetto truffle is found throughout most of Europe, as is the summer truffle, whose close cousin, the Burgundy truffle, can be found as far north as Sweden. You need more warmth for the Périgord black truffle. Large chunks of North America have native truffles and plantings of European species. Climates and soils suitable for truffle-growing exist in southern Africa, South America and Australia. Anyone with some suitable land or a large garden can have a go, if you're prepared to accept that there are no guarantees of success, and you're willing to wait for ten years (or more). It might even be possible to grow a truffle tree in a large pot on a patio.

There are ground rules you have to follow, however. You can't just stick a tree into any piece of ground and expect to get truffles. You need to match your local climate and soil to a suitable species of truffle, find a good source of infected trees, plant them away from other trees and competing fungi, and then nurse the seedlings to maturity.

In the next chapter you'll find some notes about the climatic and soil requirements of the various truffles that are now being cultivated. If you live somewhere as warm as central and southern France, the Périgord black truffle is a possibility; but if you lack that sort of summer heat, you can still consider the Burgundy truffle or bianchetto. US residents might also want to consider Oregon white truffles, but at the time of writing they're proving to be a tough nut for truffle-tree nurseries to crack. Although cold winters are not a problem for the truffles or the trees, if the ground freezes regularly to a significant depth, any truffles that do form will be badly damaged.

Black truffles prefer dry climates. Good rainfall at the right time of year (mid to late summer) is thought to be important in triggering fruiting, but too much water can cause problems. Continuously wet ground may encourage other fungi to replace the truffle, or young truffles may rot before they have time to mature.

Most European species require slightly alkaline soils. In terms of pH, the standard measure of acidity and alkalinity, black truffle soils are usually above pH7.8, where 7.0 is neutral. Soils in areas of high rainfall tend to be acid: pH6.0 or below. Alkaline soils are usually derived from limestone parent rock, but it is normally possible to treat acid soils with lime and raise their pH into the right range. In New Zealand, soils well below pH6.0 have been treated with lime and brought up to the right levels for Périgord black truffle, and truffles have been produced, so it is possible to cheat — if you're careful. You need to get a good soil test to establish the soil acidity and measure other parameters such as levels of minerals and nutrients. If you need to add lime, then this is the rule of thumb we use: 2 tonnes of lime per hectare will raise the pH by o.1. Make sure that your lime is low in phosphorus, and add it as a mixture of fine granules and larger lumps. The fine stuff will react fastest and get your soil pH moving up, while the larger stuff will take longer to break down and give you a long-lasting buffer. Plough the site as deeply as possible, and work the lime in right through the soil. Then you have to sit back and wait. The speed at which the soil pH changes depends on lots of factors, but the most critical is rainfall. One good wet winter might be all you need. But don't be tempted to plant until you're sure the soil pH is in the right range. Plant too early, and the truffle fungus might disappear.

In Europe, in the truffles' natural habitat they have to compete with lots of other fungi. As soon as a tree sends out a new root, all the mycorrhizal fungi in the immediate vicinity will try to colonise it. If the soil conditions and host tree are just right, then the truffle will win, but that precise combination might only occur on a small part of the root volume. A little seedling that started with all its roots infected with truffle will inevitably end up with contaminants which will reduce the yield of truffle. There's no way round this problem, because the spores of competing fungi are globally distributed and will eventually find their way into a truffiere, but the wise truffle grower will try to limit the problem as much as

possible. You do this by choosing a site where trees haven't been growing for a long time, and as far away as you can get from trees that could harbour competing fungi. The risk from competing fungi also depends a great deal on where you are. In Europe, there are lots; in New Zealand, very few.

Growing truffles is really about growing trees and looking after their roots: providing a healthy host for the fungus, and the right soil conditions for the truffle to thrive. If you think of your truffière as a truffle "orchard" you will get an

It's important to start with plants that have been well mycorrhized, and with the right fungus. Here one of France's biggest truffle-tree nurseries offers plants for a sale at a food expo in Provence.

idea of what you're trying to achieve, except that instead of looking for fruit on the trees, you're trying to grow a nice healthy root system covered in truffle fungus. You need summer heat, so the site should get plenty of midsummer sun. If your local trees tend to grow with a lean because of strong winds, then you should figure on getting shelter established. This could be wind-netting on tall poles, or trees that don't harbour competing fungi. Pines and poplars are no good, but (depending on your climate) you could try olives, pittosporums, tree lucerne or Leyland cypress.

Newly planted young hazel at Limestone Hills, 1997.

An irrigation system of some sort is almost certainly going to be essential. If you reckon that your site won't need watering, your climate might be too wet for truffles. The seedling trees you will plant have a very small volume of root, and can dry out and die very rapidly, so watering is essential to get them established. Later, you may need to irrigate in order to trigger fruiting, or to prevent the soil from getting too dry after your truffles have formed. On the other hand, you don't want to water so much that you disadvantage the fungus. As a rule of thumb, you will need access to enough water to simulate a late summer thunderstorm in order to trigger fruiting. This means the equivalent of at least an inch of rain (26mm) in one go. The water should be applied through sprays, mimicking rainfall, and this will also encourage the trees to keep their roots near the surface.

If you are looking to establish a truffière as a commercial enterprise, then you will need to plan the establishment phase very carefully. Mistakes made in the first year can be very hard to put right later. Getting your layout wrong, or choosing the wrong host tree, can be impossible to correct, or expensive and time-consuming. Around the world, three trees dominate truffle nursery production: hazelnuts (known as filberts in the US; *Corylus avellana* to the botanically minded), *Quercus robur*, the English oak, and *Quercus ilex*, the evergreen, holm or holly oak. In Europe, several other tree species are used, but mainly the scrubby little oak called *Quercus pubescens*. There are other hosts too, but not many are used commercially. In New Zealand, only hazels and English oaks are currently used, but research has started on other species that may be more suitable for local conditions.

Hazels are vigorous young trees, and are generally said to encourage early truffle production. The French rule of thumb is that when you get the first hazelnuts, truffle fruiting can begin. That might be as early as four years. Oaks are slower to get going, but produce a much larger tree. Most New Zealand truffières contain a mixture of hazels and oaks, often two or three hazels to each oak, but in other parts of the world hazel-only plantations are becoming more common. If you have a choice, you should try to match your host trees to your site. English oaks don't grow well in soils that are low in iron, and that's often a problem with high-pH soils. Hazels are more tolerant of that problem. On the other hand, hazels don't like wind. Mine grow with a distinct lean.

Young evergreen oa[...] in a new planting at Hugues Martin's truffière in the Périgord.

The black truffle likes heat, so the layout of the truffière has to be carefully thought out in anywhere but the hottest climates – and especially in those that might be on the cool side. To get maximum sunlight on the soil, and therefore the maximum heating effect in summer, the rows should run north-south. The planting density depends on the rate of growth you expect to get. In warm areas, oaks can grow fast, and being a forest tree, they'll get tall and form a canopy, blocking the sun from the soil. Plant them too close together, and as they mature, your site will get cooler. That's not a problem with hazels, which won't get much bigger than three or four metres tall. My own truffière has rows five metres wide, with trees a little over three metres apart in the rows. This equates to about 660 trees per hectare, but the choice of planting density varies with local climate and host species. As a rule of thumb, warm places where trees grow fast will require lower densities than cooler sites, and my site is probably towards the cool end of the range.

Getting good advice early in the planning process is essential. If you have truffle growers in your area, talk to them. They should help you to avoid re-inventing the wheel. It is also very important to find a good nursery that sells well-infected seedlings and can provide you with solid information. Look for a company that provides guarantees of infection with the right fungus, or certification from a reputable scientific body. Don't skimp on this step, because if you pick an unreliable supplier it might take ten years to discover the problem. Once again, local knowledge will be invaluable. You'll find some pointers in the Sources section at the end of this book.

Before planting the trees, prepare the site by getting rid of any grass down the rows and working the soil so that the seedling trees and their associated fungus can get off to a good start. Spray the grass first, and when it has completely died, work the soil with a ripper, rotary hoe, plough or till to produce a good soft top 20 to 30 cm or so deep, over a width of two to three metres. Wait for a while to allow weeds to germinate, and then spray again. That should give you a good head start in the battle against weeds.

Young trees need some sort of protection from wind and the depredations of pests like rabbits. There's nothing so sad as the sight of a small tree nipped in half by a rampant rabbit, so I recommend the use of boxes or sleeves over the seedlings, and a .22 rifle. Our farm cats are also very helpful. There are many different kinds of boxes, but all need stakes or posts to anchor them. Mark out your tree positions with the stakes, and then plant each seedling so that the box will cover it when it is slipped over the stake. Plant the trees slightly deeper than the soil level in the pots they arrived in, and if they were supplied in fabric bags (as opposed to black polythene pots), slit the bags with a sharp knife to allow the little roots easy access to the soil. Keep them well watered so that they have a chance to establish a decent root system, but don't waterlog the soil or you may encourage competing fungi to take over.

In the first year, management is confined to mowing grass and keeping weeds away from the young trees. Many growers are happy to do this by using herbicides, but there have been recent suggestions that glyphosate sprays may have an adverse effect on mycorrhizae, and so I have switched to judicious use of a powerful weedeater, limiting the use of sprays to once or twice a year at most.

During the first winter you can begin pruning your trees. Oaks will require little or no work because they tend to grow from the topmost bud on the tree, so they get tall quickly and require little shaping in the early years, except perhaps to remove the occasional double leader. Hazels are an altogether different proposition, as they sucker away madly, producing vigorous new shoots all around

the base of the tree. Sometimes shoots even arise from the roots some distance away from the trunk. The hazel wants to be a thicket, and you want it to be a tree, preferably conical in shape so that the sun can get on to the ground all around the plant. Try to keep the plant to one single trunk as it grows, but if that's impossible, two or three leaders can be allowed to develop. In the second year, the hazels will begin to produce suckers around the base, and these have to be removed before they get too big and start to dominate the plant. One round in late spring and another in late summer should be enough. Sadly, the more you prune hazels, the more you stimulate the production of suckers. If you have to do a lot of shaping of any tree, "little and often" is best.

In the early spring of the second year, before bud-burst, do your second major round of soil work. Till the soil to a depth of 20 cm in strips on either side of the rows. This keeps the soil aerated, and should produce the right conditions for new roots and fungus to colonise the area. While the truffière is young, you could also do a second bit of soil work in mid-summer, but once brulées have begun to appear you should only very lightly till inside them, and only in early spring before bud-burst.

The routine for the rest of the year is straightforward. Keep the trees growing by ensuring that they have adequate moisture, but don't overwater. Mow the grass as often as required and keep an eye on the health of the trees. If you're growing Périgord black truffles, you'll know you're doing well when you see your first

Interesting agri-cultural implement #2: Hugues Martin shows off his spiked roller.

brulées, the areas of "burnt" ground round the trees that indicate that the truffle fungus is alive and well and doing its job. A brulée isn't always bare earth. Sometimes you can see the truffle working on the competing plants by making life difficult for them. As you get nearer to the tree, so the size of the plants gets smaller. Wishful thinking is also a powerful aid to brulée visibility!

To reassure yourself that all's well with your truffière, it's worth getting the roots checked by an expert from time to time. The procedure is simple. You dig up some root and look at it with a hand lens or under a microscope. The mycorrhiza of Périgord black truffle is relatively easy to see – it looks like a black coating on the fine rootlets – but others can be much harder to spot. *Scleroderma*, one of the chief fungal contaminants of truffières, is the easiest of all to see. It looks like white cobwebs filling the soil spaces. Some contamination of your truffière is inevitable, but too much might indicate problems with your management of the plantation.

Look out for suckers on your hazels, and always remove them before they get too large. Rubbing the sucker buds off the trunk is the best approach. Some professional hazel growers use chain-mail gloves, the sort butchers wear to protect their fingers from cuts, to gently rub the buds off.

Insect damage to young trees is an occasional problem in any plantation, but unless the damage is severe, it may be too difficult to get rid of. Young oaks are prone to problems with a white mil-dew on their leaves, particularly in damp weather and especially when they are growing in boxes. This can be treated with copper fungicide sprays, but there is an obvious risk that this could harm the truffle fungus in the soil, so it should be reserved for severe infections. Where I've seen it done, growers have gone to great lengths to prevent spray drips reaching the ground by using plastic sheeting around the base of the tree. Once the trees are in their third or fourth year, they'll be big enough to cope by themselves.

Depending on your soil conditions, the young trees could run into a number of problems with shortages of key nutrients and minerals. My young oaks struggled to cope with the low iron levels in my truffière, and many became chlorotic. Their leaves turned yellow, and in bad cases brown, before dropping off. After this happens the tree usually sulks, refusing to grow until you give it some iron, either as a foliar spray or as a soil drench. It can take years for an oak to recover from the shock, and many simply give up and die. As a result, I've replaced more than half of the oaks I originally planted. A spring soil drench with a micro-granular iron chelate before bud burst is one treatment, but if low iron is a problem, you are probably best to avoid oaks completely. Other mineral and nutrient deficiencies can lead to leaf yellowing, and there is no universal solution. Consult a local expert, and be careful that you do nothing that could cause problems for the mycorrhiza.

Your first truffle harvest could happen as early as the fourth winter after planting, particularly if your trees have grown vigorously and are showing good brulées. Périgord black growers may have to wait for up to ten years before fruiting commences, but from year five on, their chances should be increasing rapidly. Bianchetto truffles don't produce brulées, but are said to be particularly likely to fruit early. Burgundy truffles are more like their Périgord cousins, but they don't always produce brulées. In any event, you will need to have trained your dog, or arranged the services of one, from at least the fifth winter onwards. For hints and tips about looking for truffles, refer back to Chapter 12, but if you are particularly fortunate, you may find one fruiting near the surface, just pushing out through the soil. In all but one of New Zealand's producing truffières the first truffle finds were made by an educated eye spotting them poking through the soil. In loose crumbly soil, it may even be possible to spot truffles as they swell during autumn, because they can push the soil upwards, leaving characteristic little cracks or volcano-like mounds on the soil surface.

And what do you do with the truffles when you've got them? Eat them, of course. But if you're in this as a business and want to make some sort of income, then you are going to have a means of getting them to market. In France and Italy, as we've seen, there is a well established local network of markets, and wholesalers who ship truffles all around the world, but in other countries it may not be that simple. A fresh truffle only has a shelf life of 7–10 days, so the best approach is to look for local outlets. Good restaurants are the obvious market, but delicatessens or other up-market food retailers may also be interested. Once again, a little local knowledge is a useful thing, and truffle growers nearby may be able to help. Be sure to check out any local regulations regarding the quality and sale of truffles. In parts of France, for instance, it is illegal to sell black truffle before mid-December.

CHAPTER TWENTY ONE

The Truffle Guide

This is a basic guide to the major truffle species eaten around the world. It isn't definitive, and doesn't go into all the characteristics that mycologists use when identifying fungi. It will, however, give you a start on telling one truffle from another, and provide some basic information on what grows where and with which kinds of tree.

The Périgord black truffle. A fine specimen harvested in July 2005 in Ashburton, New Zealand.

There are hundreds of different species of hypogeous, truffle-like fungi, but only a dozen or so are considered worth eating. Their whole lifestyle revolves around being eaten by all sorts of animals, so it is fairly safe to assume that most will not be poisonous - but that's not the same as being good to eat. Truffles bought in a market or from reputable wholesalers or retailers will (or ought to be) exactly what they're claimed to be, but if you've been out in the woods and your dog has dug up something you think might be a truffle, then there's one basic rule to follow: if in doubt, throw it out. In other words, if you cannot be one hundred percent sure of the identification of the truffle (or any other mushroom), then don't eat it.

The first part of this list deals with the major edible truffles, and I have arbitrarily divided them into "black" and "white" truffles. This is based on external appearance – skin colour – and not on the colour of the flesh inside. I then list some of the commoner non-edible truffles, and some that can be confused for the real thing.

Black truffles

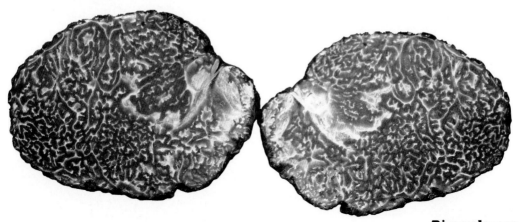

Tuber melanosporum
Périgord black truffle
mélano
tartufo nero pregiato

Ripe melanosporum *cut in half to show characteristic network of white veins in dark flesh.*
(Tim Terry)

The ripe fruiting bodies of *Tuber melanosporum* are black-skinned and can be anything from hazelnut-sized up to the size of a grapefruit. They are usually roughly spherical, but may be lobed or distorted owing to rocks or stones in the soil. The skin is covered with pronounced pyramid-shaped warts. The flesh is a dark purplish black, with fine white veins forming maze-like patterns through it. In unripe truffles the flesh is brownish white, darkening with maturity through brown to black. The aroma is powerful, with sweet forest-floor notes.

Ripe truffles can be found from late November to March in the northern hemisphere, with the peak season being January. The southern hemisphere season is May to August, peaking in July. This species grows in high-pH (alkaline, from pH 7.6 upwards) limestone soils in association with various oaks, principally *Quercus ilex* (evergreen, holm or holly oak), and *Quercus pubescens*. Hazels (*Corylus avellena*) and English oaks (*Quercus robur*) are also good hosts, and widely planted in truffieres around the world.

Tuber melanosporum is adapted to withstand hot summers and dry conditions, but prolonged drought severely reduces production. It is found in the wild in northeast Spain, central and southern France and northern and central Italy.

Tuber aestivum

summer truffle, common truffle
scorzone, tartufo estivo
truffe d'été, truffe de la St Jean, truffe
blanche d'été, maïenque

This is the commonest truffle in Europe, found from North Africa to Sweden and from Britain to Russia. The skin is black, and covered with pronounced pyramid-shaped warts, like those of the Perigord black but often larger. The flesh varies from cream to light brown in colour, and has similar veins to those seen in *melanosporum*. The aroma is much less intense. Summer truffle may ripen as early as April or May, and continue fruiting until autumn. It prefers limestone-rich soils (but isn't as picky as *melanosporum*), and grows in association with oaks, hazels and beeches. It doesn't tolerate drying out, so expect to find it in shady, moist conditions.

Swedish **aestivum,** *showing large pyramidal warts on skin.* (*Christina Wedén*)

Tuber uncinatum

Burgundy truffle
tartufo uncinato, tartufo nero di Fragno
truffe du Bourgogne, truffe grise, grise de Bourgogne

The Burgundy truffle is a very close cousin of the summer truffle, close enough for some researchers to insist that what we call summer truffle is just unripe Burgundy. To complicate matters, *aestivum* was named first, so under the rules for species names, Burgundy truffle should be called *Tuber aestivum*. However, some genetic

Flesh of **Tuber aesti**vum, *showing varying stages of ripeness least ripe to the left, ripest on the right. Note the similarity in the veining to its close relative,* **Tuber melanosporum.**
(*Christina Wedén*)

studies suggest that it is more or less identical; others that it differs in some important respects. For practical purposes, the main difference is that the Burgundy truffle ripens later in the year, from late autumn into winter, has a more pronounced aroma and flavour, and its flesh, when ripe, is a darker brown. Although named after the Burgundy region of central eastern France, it is found over a wide area of Europe in association with many different host trees, including pines, oaks and hazels. There has been a surge in interest in this species in France, where it is being widely planted in truffières. Experiments are also under way in New Zealand, where it is hoped that it will help growers to extend the season when fresh truffles are available for consumption and export.

Tuber brumale
  winter truffle
  tartufo invernale
  brumale

Tuber brumale likes similar conditions to the Périgord black, and is a major competitor in the wild and in truffières in Europe. It can cope with cooler and damper climates, and has even been reported from Britain. When truffière conditions are not ideal, *brumale* can displace *melanosporum*. The skin is black and covered with warts, though these are generally smaller and less pronounced than those of *melanosporum*, and the flesh is usually less dark, varying from grey-brown to grey-black when mature, and the veining is coarser and less convoluted. The aroma is intense, but not so pleasant as the Périgord black: it is sometimes described as similar to fermenting or rotting fruit. The season is December to March. A close relative, *Tuber brumale* var. *moschatum* (tartufo moscato in Italy, musquée in France) has only one major difference. It has a pronounced musk note to its aroma.

*French **uncinatum** expert Gerard Chevalier of INRA admires one of the young oaks infected with **uncinatum** at Limestone Hills.*

The Bagnoli truffle, cut in half to show t. characteristic "bow or cup-shaped depre sion. Much esteeme in Bagnoli, but nowhere else. (*Alessan Zambonelli*)

Tuber mesentericum
Bagnoli truffle
tartufo nero ordinario
mésentérique, truffe de Bagnoli

The Bagnoli truffle is found in central Italy and in many parts of France, Switzerland, Germany and Hungary. It has a very black skin with large warts, rather similar to those of *aestivum*, but the spherical shape has a characteristic depression or "bowl" in it. The flesh is whitish in immature truffles, turning brownish, with white veins often seeming to radiate from the "bowl". The aroma can be quite intense, but is very phenolic (like carbolic soap), and this limits its attraction as an edible species (outside Bagnoli, at least). However, experienced users suggest that a brief period of heating (in a cream sauce, say) drives off the unpleasant aroma, leaving a good truffle flavour.

Tuber macrosporum
large-spored truffle
tartufo nero liscio

This might also be described as the "smooth black truffle" because liscio means smooth in Italian. It has a less warty skin than *melanosporum*, *aestivum* or *brumale*, and the colour varies from black to reddish brown. The flesh has broader veins than are seen in melanosporum, and when ripe is brown to reddish brown. The aroma is garlicky, similar to that of *Tuber magnatum* but less intense. The large-spored truffle ripens from July to November, and seldom grows larger than an egg. One Italian expert considers it to be a good edible truffle, but it's often confused with other, inferior species and so not valued in the marketplace. It grows with poplars, willows, oaks and chestnuts, and has been found in Britain, so it's probably fairly widely distributed in Europe.

Chinese truffles
Tuber pseudoexcavatum, Tuber indicum, Tuber sinense, Tuber himalayense, Tuber pseudohimalayense
Chinese truffle
truffe de Chine

A selection of Chinese truffles. From left: an unidentified **Tuber** *species,* **Tuber sinense** *and* **Tuber excavatum.**
(*Yu Fuqiang*)

Chinese truffles are usually called *Tuber indicum* in Europe, but the black truffles found in China include *Tuber pseudoexcavatum*, *Tuber indicum*, *Tuber sinense*, *Tuber himalayense* and *Tuber pseudohimalayense*. A final determination of names remains to be made. Many of these species are very similar to *Tuber melanosporum*, with black warty skin and dark flesh with fine white veins, but the aroma is less intense. One major difference is that the flesh is more rubbery, like Emmental cheese. French scientists have developed a DNA test to distinguish between *melanosporum* and *indicum*, so they can enforce consumer protection and labelling regulations.

Both species grow in association with oaks and pines, on the eastern flanks of the Himalaya in the Yunnan and Sichuan provinces of China, and *himalayensis* on the higher slopes and in Tibet. Other similar species are said to occur in the southern Himalayas, but as far as I can establish they are not very well known or commercially exploited.

Oregon brown and black truffles. (Charle. Lefevre)

Leucangium carthusianum
Oregon black truffle
chartreuse truffle (France)

This species was discovered to be a good edible truffle in Oregon in the 1990s. It occurs in association with Douglas fir, especially in young plantations, in a broad swathe of the northwestern Pacific coast, from California to southern British Columbia. In Europe it is found with other tree species and has never been considered edible. The truffles have a black skin and very dark flesh with thin white veins, and the aroma is complex and fruity. They vary from golf ball to baseball-sized, and ripen from October to February. Oregon black truffles are less common than the Oregon white truffles, and command higher prices. Their unique kind of sweetness (not the sweetness of sugar: more the flowery sweetness of an aromatic white wine) has led to their being used with desserts.

Unnamed brown Oregon truffle, possibly *Picoa* n. sp.

Oregon also has a brown truffle (left, above) which appears in reasonable quantities in some years – 2005 was a very good year. It hasn't been given a scientific name, but is perhaps a member of the genus *Picoa*. It is also highly regarded and can command higher prices than the Oregon black.

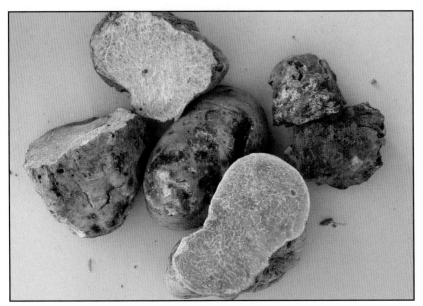

Tuber magnatum: *if you had this much on the table in front of you, the smell would be overpowering. Note the vein structure in the cut flesh – much finer than in* **melanosporum.** *(Alessandra Zambonelli)*

White truffles

Tuber magnatum
Italian white truffle
truffe blanche d'Italie, truffe du Piémont

The most expensive truffle in the world is found only in Italy, Croatia, Serbia and perhaps in tiny parts of the extreme southeast corner of France and one valley in southern Switzerland. It ranges from walnut-sized to over 1 kg, and is usually shaped like a knobbly sphere. The skin is brownish yellow and quite thick, while the flesh is pale brown in immature specimens, becoming much darker when fully ripe. It grows in association with poplars, willows and European limes, in moist, deep lime rich soils that are well aerated and free-draining. White truffles can occur in both wooded valley bottoms and around single trees.

The aroma is incredibly powerful and very hard to describe: most often said to be garlicky, sometimes with a suggestion of parmesan cheese. Once sniffed and tasted, it is never forgotten. The season runs from September to December, with October being the peak month. It has never been successfully cultivated in truffières, though attempts to work out how to persuade this culinary treasure to infect seedling trees are continuing in laboratories and nurseries in Europe, the USA and New Zealand.

A good selection of Tuber borchii fruit-bodies. The flesh is darker than magnatum, and the veins broader. (Alessandra Zambonelli)

Tuber borchii (also called *Tuber albidum*)
bianchetto, marzuolo, tartufo di pineta
truffe blanche, blanquette

This is the closest truffle to *magnatum* in appearance, aroma and flavour: close enough to be sometimes passed off as the real thing. It is usually fairly small, though in well-aerated soils can grow to the size of an orange. The skin is brownish white, and the flesh reddish brown with large white veins. The aroma is garlicky, and less intense than that of *magnatum*. The truffle ripens from December to March. It grows throughout Europe, including Britain, and in association with a wide variety of trees, but often with pines in Italy. It is a vigorous fungus, and has been successfully cultivated in truffières in Italy, on the Adriatic coast near Ravenna, near Rome, and on Sardinia. Most of the Italian successes have been on lime-rich soils (pH 7.3 to 7.6). In Britain, *borchii* is most often found on lime-rich soils with larch and beech. Most finds of *borchii* have come from south-west England, but it has also been reported from as far north as Strathclyde. It is not widely appreciated in the marketplace because it is often confused with inferior white truffle species, though this should change as cultivated truffles become more available. New Zealand has over 20 experimental *borchii* plantations, and production should (we hope) begin soon.

Tuber gibbosum, the Oregon grey, or spring white truffle. *(Charles Lefevre)*

Oregon white truffles
Tuber oregonensis
Oregon winter white truffle
Tuber gibbosum
Oregon grey truffle, Oregon spring white truffle
Tuber wheeleri

These three species are often all lumped together and called Oregon white truffles. Like the Oregon black truffle, they grow in association with Douglas fir, especially in young plantations, from California to southern British Columbia. They have a good aroma and excellent taste, and fully mature specimens have more than held their own against *Tuber magnatum*.

Tuber oregonense is found from October to February, but is it at its best from mid-December to January in most years. It has an orangey-brown skin and brownish interior when fully ripe, and is usually fairly small.

Tuber gibbosum ripens from February through to spring, and although it looks very similar, it can grow considerably larger – up to 300 g.

Tuber wheeleri is rare, and difficult to distinguish from its close cousins. It's named for Oregon truffle pioneer Dan Wheeler, who is reported to have been finding large quantities of it since it was so named!

Tuber lyonii, *the Texas or pecan truf- fle.* (Charles Lefevre)

Tuber lyonii
pecan truffle, Texas truffle

The pecan truffle is found in many parts of North America, from Texas to southern Ontario and Quebec in Canada, and in associa- tion with a wide variety of trees. It is a smallish truffle, commonly found in irrigated pecan nut orchards in the southwest US. The skin is orangey brown and the flesh pale brown with white veins. The aroma and flavour can be good, but these truffles are harvested by raking and so quality is variable. They ripen from August to November.

Desert truffles
Terfezia and Tirmania spp.

An Egyptian exampl of **Terfezia truffles,** *sliced ready for cool ing.* (John Feeney/Saudi Aramco World/PADIA)

There are more than 30 different species of desert truffle belonging to the genera Terfezia and Tirmania. The Kalahari truffle is *Terfezia pfielii*, while *bouderi* and *Terfezia claveryi* can be found from Morocco to the Middle East. *Tirmania pinoyi* is common in southern Morocco, and is called Terfass blanc de Tafilet. All grow in association with plants adapted to the desert and semi-arid

climates of southern Europe, North Africa and the Middle East, especially *Helianthemum* species.

Other truffles

Tuber maculatum

The name *maculatum* means spotted or blotched. This is one of a number of whitish truffles with brown flesh that are easily mistaken for *Tuber borchii*. It is edible, and can smell reasonably attractive when fully ripe. It is distributed throughout Europe, and sometimes common. It has also arrived in New Zealand, perhaps on the roots of trees brought in by European settlers. It grows in association with a wide variety of trees and ripens in autumn. Other similar looking species include *Tuber rapaeodorum* (the species name means "smelling like turnips"), *Tuber puberulum*, *Tuber dryophilum* and *Tuber foetidum* – which has the dubious-sounding English name of "stinking truffle" and so is probably not very nice to eat.

Tuber dryophilum: *one of a number of whitish truffles easily mistaken for borchii.* (Alessandra Zambonelli)

Tuber rufum
   red truffle
   rufum, nez de chien

Tuber rufum is common throughout Europe, and has also been found in New Zealand. The French name "dog's nose" gives a good impression of its shape, which often shows a pronounced groove in its reddish brown, warty skin. The flesh is yellowish or brownish white with both white and dark veins. The truffles are rather small.

A final note of caution...
There are hundreds of other species of truffle-like fungi, most of which are easily distinguished from any of the culinary or commercially important species. *Choiromyces meandriformis* is more of a problem. It is widely distributed in Europe and the commonest large white truffle in Britain. It can be mistaken for *Tuber magnatum*, although it doesn't smell much like the real thing, and can cause stomach upsets if eaten in large quantities. The veins in the flesh are distinctive, however. *Balsamia vulgaris* can also look a bit like *magnatum*, but has a redder skin and paler, less-veined flesh.

Sources

If you want to know more about truffles — and there's plenty to explore that I haven't covered, or haven't had space to do full justice to — then the following selection of books, web sites and contacts will be of interest. In it I list some of the major books that have helped me in my researches, but it should be noted that the literature in English is limited, and there's a lot been published in French and Italian, much of which I have not had access to. I also include some of the better recipe books that I've encountered, and for those who might want to try growing their own, there are contact details for some of the world's larger truffle tree nurseries, and two of the major truffle grower organisations.

Books & other publications

The Black Truffle, by Dr. Ian Hall, Gordon Brown and James Byars, Second edition, 1994; (*Crop & Food Research, Lincoln, New Zealand*), republished as a CD ROM, 2001, ISBN 0-478-10824-9. There have been very few books on truffles in English (other than some translations and cookbooks), and this is far and away the best of them. It covers the history, uses and cultivation of the Périgord black truffle, and is still the reference work for growers in New Zealand. Unfortunately, the information it contains is now getting rather long in the tooth, and I am eagerly awaiting Dr. Hall's follow-up, currently in preparation.

La truffe: Guide technique de trufficulture, by Jean-Michel Ricard, First edition, 2003; ISBN 2-87911-125-0 (*Éditions du Centre technique interprofessionnel des fruits et légumes, Paris*). A very comprehensive and extremely well illustrated guide to truffles and truffle growing in France.

Le Livre de la Truffe, by Bérnard Duc-Maugé & Bernard Duplessy, First edition, 1997; ISBN 2-85744-968-2 (*Édisud, Aix-en-*

Provence). Covers the world of French truffles in considerable detail with good sections on the truffle business and history of truffle consumption.

Norme Pratiche Per La Coltivazione Del Tartufo, by Ecoplanning s.r.l., First edition, 1992 (*Ministero Dell'Agricoltura e Delle Foreste, Italy*). Good general guide to Italy's truffles and how to grow them.

Des Truffes en général et de la Rabasse en particulier, by Jean-Marie Rocchia, First edition, 1995; ISBN 2-87923-054-3 (*Éditions A. Barthélemy, Avignon*). An English translation of this marvellous, good-humoured look at truffles in Provence was published in 1995 as **Black Diamond And Other Truffles** (ISBN 2-87923-050-0). It can occasionally be found at Amazon and other on-line booksellers. Has a very good chapter about the arrival of Chinese truffles in France. The French edition is not a difficult read for anyone with a smattering of French and a good dictionary, and it's well worth the intellectual effort.

British Truffles, A Revision Of British Hypogeous Fungi, by D Pegler, B Spooner and T Young, First edition, 1993; ISBN 0-947643-39-7 (*Royal Botanic Gardens, Kew, London*). An unashamedly academic tome, with details of all the truffle records held at the Herbarium Library at Kew. Not bedtime reading by any means, but interesting to anyone who wants to learn about truffles in Britain.

A Passion For Mushrooms, by Antonio Carluccio, First edition, 1989; ISBN 1-85145-113-7 (*Pavilion Books, London*). Excellent mushroom identification and cooking book from the doyen of mushroom chefs. Based firmly in the Italian tradition — I've been cooking from it for 15 years.

Complete Mushroom Book: The Quiet Hunt, by Antonio Carluccio, First edition, 2003; ISBN 1-844000-40-0 (*Quadrille Publishing Ltd, London*). Beautifully illustrated and comprehensive fungal cookbook, with a good guide to identifying the mushrooms you're likely to find in Europe.

Le Grand Livre De La Truffe, by Pierre-Jean & Jacques Pébeyre, First edition, 1988; ISBN 2-221-05511-X (*Éditions Daniel Brand/Robert Laffont, Paris*). Good collection of recipes from the house of Pébeyre, including all the classics of French cuisine.

Truffes, by Pierre-Jean Pébeyre & Ken Hom, First French edition, 2001; ISBN 2-012-36629-5 (*Hachette Livre, Paris*). Huge quantities of truffles must have been used in the creation of this book. Fabulous photography and recipes that range from French (and Pébeyre family) classics to Asian-influenced dishes.

Web sites

As this book went to press, a Google search for "truffle" produced a list of 731,000 web pages that used the word somewhere. If you exclude all the ones about chocolate balls, and those people who have used the word because they like the sound, that's still an awful lot of information, and you can spend ages hunting through it all. Here are a few starting points:

I "blog" events in the truffle world and at Limestone Hills on the Limestone Hills web site, http://www.limestonehills.co.nz/Down%20On%20The%20Farm/index.html.

A similar sort of thing is the "Mag de la Truffe", http://truffiere.free.fr/magdelatruffe/, operated by a French truffle grower. Lots of interesting material and discussion (in French, of course).

The village of St. Alvère in the Périgord was one of the first to offer truffles over the internet, and in season it's a good place to visit to see what prices are like (it also has a discussion board): http://www.truffe-perigord-noir.com/default.asp.

The North American Truffling Society, http://www.natruffling.org/, is a good place to find out more about the indigenous truffles of North America.

Nurseries

This is a far from complete list, but it will get you started if you want to source quality truffle-infected plants.

New Zealand: *Crop & Food Research*, Private Bag 4704, Christchurch. Tel: +64 3 325 6400. Fax: +64 3 325 2074. http://www.crop.cri.nz/home/index.jsp.

Australia: *Tasmanian Truffle Enterprises Ltd*, 844 Mole Creek Road, Deloraine 7304, Tasmania, Australia. Tel: +61 03 6363 6194 Fax: +61 03 6363 6196. http://www.tastruffles.com.au/.

Treetech Treetec Consulting Pty Ltd, PO Box 1920 Subiaco, Western Australia 6008. Tel: +61 1300 65 33 58. Fax +61 8 93815113. http://www.treetec.com.au/.

North America: *New World Truffières*, PO Box 5802, Eugene, OR 97405. Tel: +1 (541) 513 4176. http://www.truffletree.com/.

Garland Gourmet Mushrooms & Truffles, Inc., 3020 Ode Turner Road, Hillsborough, NC 27278. Tel: +1 (919) 732-3041. Fax: +1 (919) 732-6037. www.garlandtruffles.com.

Britain: *Truffle UK Ltd*, PO Box 5389, Cattistock, Dorchester, Dorset, DT2 0XN. Tel: +44 (0) 1935 83819. Fax: +44 (0) 1935 83820. Mobile: +44 (0) 7767 494973. http://www.truffle-uk.co.uk/index.

php. Will also supply to Europe.

    France: *Agri-Truffe*, Domaine de Lalanne, 33490 Saint Maixant. Tel: + 33 (0) 5 56 62 00 53. Fax: +33 (0)5 56 62 09 63. http://www.agri-truffe.fr/.

    Pépinières Robin, Le Village, 05500 Saint Laurent Du Cros. Tel: +33 (0) 4 92 50 43 16. Fax: +33 (0) 4 92 50 47 57. http://www.robin-pepinieres.com/.

    There's a list of many other French tree producers at http://www.pommiers.com/chene-truffier/truffe.htm.

    Italy: *Raggi Vivai di Raggi Giordano*, Via Cerchia di S.Egidio, 3000, 47023 Cesena (FC).Tel: +39 (0)547 382171. Fax +39 (0)547 631874. http://www.raggivivai.it/collaboraconlanatura/uk.asp.

    Centro Sperimentale di Tartuficoltura, Via Macina, 1, 61048, S.Angelo in Vado (PU). Tel: +39 (0)722 88849/88008. http://www.agri.marche.it/Aree%20tematiche/Tartufi/. Gigi Gregori's nursery, pictured on page 111.

    Vivaio Il Campino, Siena. Contact via web site: http://campino.provincia.siena.it/index.htm.

Grower Associations

    The New Zealand Truffle Association, Box 29045, Ngaio, Wellington. Tel: +64 4 939 8441. Fax: 64 977 4794. http://www.southern-truffles.co.nz/index.htm.

    Fédération Francaise Des Trufficulteurs, 7 bis rue du Louvre, F - 75001 Paris. Tel: +33 01 42 36 03 29. Fax: +33 01 42 36 26 93. http://www.fft-tuber.org/fft.asp.

Acknowledgements & photo credits

Many people have helped me in the course of the preparation of this book. Scientists studying edible mycorrhizal fungi have been particularly helpful, correcting my errors and pointing me in the right direction. In New Zealand, Dr. Ian Hall's former team at Crop & Food Research have always been willing to help; Professor Wang Yun provided valuable input to the section on Chinese truffles, and Carolyn Dixon did her best to find me a *Tuber rufum* to photograph. In Italy, Alessandra Zambonelli of the University of Bologna not only opened doors when I toured there a few years ago, but gave generously of her time and expertise, both scientific and culinary. She also introduced me to "Gigi" Gregori, my most excellent host and guide to the truffle world in Acqualagna. Mario

Honrubia of the University of Murcia in Spain kindly read the section on Spain, and Christina Wedén ensured that I got my Swedish facts straight. Charles Lefevre of New World Truffières in Oregon helped me to understand the truffles of the Pacific Northwest. All (except Gigi) have visited me at Limestone Hills, and all are welcome back. It goes without saying, but I'll say it anyway: all the mistakes in this book are mine, and most of the good things due to their help.

This book would not be the same without the tremendous help I've received in finding pictures from all corners of the world. Eric Boa put me in touch with Yu Fuqiang at the Kunming Institute of Botany in Yunnan Province, China, who supplied the marvellous pictures of China and Chinese truffles. Charles Lefevre provided excellent pictures of Oregon truffles, and Franklin and Betty Garland helped with pictures of their operation in Maryland. Tim Terry in Tasmania and Nick Malajczuk in Western Australia were both generous with their time and photographs. Christina Wedén supplied a terrific selection of pictures from her Gotland truffières. I'm particularly grateful to Alessandra Zambonelli for her help with pictures for the truffle guide. Thanks also to Dr. Ian Hall, Andy Mikkelsen, Patricia Nelson, Nigel Hadden-Paton and Adrian Cole, and the Public Affairs Digital Image Archive at Saudi Aramco.

The production of *The Truffle Book* relied a great deal on the advice and assistance I've received from friends and colleagues. Mike Bradstock supported the idea from the start, and has been a diligent and perceptive editor and publishing consultant. Without his help, this book would never have reached the bookshops. My old friend and colleague Tony Cohen was kind enough to provide a design for the book at long range from his studio in London. All the good looking stuff is his, the infelicities mine. Craig McNeill drew the maps and imagined what Alfred Collins might have looked like. Barry Flewellyn did the author mug shot on the back cover, and managed to hide a multitude of sins...

The truffle growers of New Zealand have been unfailingly helpful and friendly from the early days of my involvement in the business. Working with (and for) them remains a pleasure.

Limestone Hills, September 2005

Index

Notes

Notes

Notes

Notes